ELECTRONIC COMPONENTS

Other Constructor's Guides

Electronic Diagrams
Printed Circuit Assembly

In Preparation

Simple Circuit Building
Practical Electronic Project Building
Project Planning and Building

ELECTRONIC COMPONENTS

MORRIS A COLWELL

NEWNES TECHNICAL BOOKS

THE BUTTERWORTH GROUP

ENGLAND
Butterworth & Co (Publishers) Ltd
London: 88 Kingsway, WC2B 6AB

AUSTRALIA
Butterworths Pty Ltd
Sydney: 586 Pacific Highway, NSW 2067
Melbourne: 343 Little Collins Street, 3000
Brisbane: 240 Queen Street, 4000

CANADA
Butterworth & Co (Canada) Ltd
Scarborough: 2265 Midland Avenue, Ontario M1P 4S1

NEW ZEALAND
Butterworths of New Zealand Ltd
Wellington: 26–28 Waring Taylor Street, 1

SOUTH AFRICA
Butterworth & Co (South Africa) (Pty) Ltd
Durban: 152–154 Gale Street

First published in 1976 by Newnes Technical Books
A Butterworth imprint

© Butterworth & Co (Publishers) Ltd. 1976

ISBN 0 408 00202 6

Typeset by Butterworths LPD
Printed and bound in England by The Pitman Press, Bath

INTRODUCTION

In compiling a book on electronic components, there inevitably arises the question of what the scope of this topic will be. So often does one find information on the theory and manufacture, which can be not only irrelevant to one's needs, but also not very helpful to constructors. What is often required is some practical guidance on the choosing and using aspects. In a book of limited proportions there must be some points that are not included and it will be largely through the constructor's personal and practical experiences that he will learn most. What can be done, however, is to take an objective look at some of the more frequent problems that arise with newcomers to the art, and perhaps discuss some of the less obvious points.

This book does not claim to be anywhere near an exhaustive treatment of the subject; to do so would occupy very many more pages, which inevitably leads to higher wastage to the user. What is provided in a readily digested form are some useful hints that one acquires through experience and a small amount of 'textbook' style support information. Photographs and drawings help to identify some of the components.

The text is aimed at constructors with a small measure of experience and an understanding of common everyday terms used. The book will appeal particularly to hobbyists and technicians, and will most probably provide a useful support for students and trainees, and especially to readers of the popular constructional type magazines.

In compiling the information given, the author has received considerable co-operation from a number of firms and organisations who have kindly supplied photographs and information. To all of these the author extends his thanks and, where appropriate, acknowledgement is given against photographs that have been used.

M. A. C.

CONTENTS

1 Getting started

To most people who acquire an interest in electronics, or some particular branch of the subject, it is usually as a result of a fascination in the end result and a curiosity in how it is achieved. No matter what your particular interest, whether professional or amateur, be it in entertainment, instrumentation or industrial control, you will be involved in the practical aspects at some stage, requiring the use of wire cutters and soldering iron to assemble components. The urge to become practical, to construct or create, is a natural feeling with most people who become involved, since it has been said that electronics is an art as much as a science. Without practical experience, the theory one learns remains sterile and unproductive; without knowledge the creation cannot take form.

But how does one start to go about a creation? It is one thing to possess a handful of components; it is often a very different matter to make them up into a form whereby they do a useful job, without finishing in a cloud of smoke.

You must choose the right components and adopt principles of assembly appropriate to the end result, that is if you are to achieve what you set out to do. There is an enormous variety of components readily available to constructors; how does one go about selecting the right one for the job in hand? If the circuit designer presents a theoretical circuit with component values, the constructor should be able to convert his design into a working model. Most designers make up their own circuits to prove that they will work, then pass on the necessary information for others to do likewise. In most cases, it is possible to make up given designs successfully, provided that either some practical experience is assumed or that constructional information is provided, but this is not always the case.

1

There are special factors that may prohibit the free interpretation of design or layouts, unless the constructor is prepared to sort out problems of faulty operation. In a book of this kind, it is not expected that the reader will be fully experienced in every conceivable aspect of construction work. He will, most likely, specialise or guide his activities into a fairly narrow field of interest and learn about the special problems of that particular aspect. What this book aims to achieve is to provide a basic grounding in the practical aspects of using and selecting components, what they can or cannot do, how they are likely to behave, what special problems they might present. To cover the whole subject adequately would occupy several hundreds of pages and it is not the intention to indulge in full analyses of theory as well as practice, since this information is available elsewhere. A ready reference for the constructor must be concise and it should be possible to find the necessary information quickly while construction work proceeds.

Tools

Before starting practical work, the constructor should have the necessary tools and be in a position to recognise the components he is using from their appearance and markings; experience alone will make him proficient in doing this quickly and effectively. One should never become deterred by the sheer complexity of the job or the variations of different types of components that are available. It is not possible to know everything about them before starting and it is only to be expected that questions are bound to be raised at some time or other.

In conjunction with the companion volumes in the Constructor's Guide series, the reader will be well equipped in a fairly short time to assimilate the implications of practical project work and even learn something about the theory as well. He should then be able to gain confidence in tackling those projects that may have eluded his experience.

The first and most important tools that he will need to get started will include small diagonal or side cutting pliers, tapered long-nosed wiring pliers, screwdrivers (chisel bladed) and at least one, preferably two, soldering irons. All hand held tools should be efficiently insulated over the whole area of the handles and soldering irons (used in the UK) should be earthed.

When choosing wire cutters, the best test is to try cutting very thin tissue paper with them. This will give a good indication how effective the cutting edges are over the full length of them. The cutters should be comfortable to hold single-handed without causing undue strain on the finger muscles, either through stiffness at the pivot joint or through unbalanced weight. The two parts should move freely throughout the whole of their travel when manipulated, but must not be so free that they are loose or sloppy at the joint. The two cutting edges should line up correctly without spaces between them; this can be checked by holding them up to the light with the jaws normally closed.

The price of such wire cutters can vary considerably, but it should not be automatically assumed that the most expensive is necessarily the best to get; there are some less expensive types that can be good value for money if you are prepared to inspect a few samples and select the best of them. Many tools are prepacked in plastic bubble packs for shop displays; this is a pity because it is almost impossible to handle and inspect them properly before committing yourself to buying.

Similarly with long-nosed wiring pliers, the handles should be free moving without being loose. The jaws should be tapered to a truly aligned pair of very narrow tips, preferably not larger than one-eighth of an inch wide (3 mm). The faces of the jaws should be in contact for at least the end ½ inch (12 mm), but preferably for the full length. Always remember that wiring pliers should never be used as a spanner, otherwise you can expect the jaws to suffer bending or even breakage.

Combined long-nosed wiring and cutting pliers can be useful and economic if they are of a comparable quality as described. It will pay to buy good tools to start with; they are more likely to give you long service. However, this type of pliers is unable to perform cutting tasks in very confined spaces that the diagonal cutters can do by use of the tips. Check also that the wire cutting blades meet properly and carry out the checks described for diagonal cutters.

Soldering

Soldering irons of various sizes and bit shapes can be bought, some included in kit packs with spare bits, solder, instruction booklets and sometimes a stand. There is a popular misconception that the large irons are hotter than the smaller types within the same comparable family. The fact is that the larger the iron, and bit, the greater is the heat retention property. It is a little bit like a power supply in that the heavier duty it is, the more work it will do and the larger the load it will handle. Therefore, the larger irons are best for soldering tag joints and metal plates. This could be a 25 watt iron or something near to it. However, there are risks in attempting to solder on to printed circuit boards with this size, particularly if the copper pads are small or thin; the iron is likely to melt away the copper and overheat the base material as well, leaving an unsightly mess and possibly a 'dry' joint. For printed circuit work and any components that may be sensitive to heat, such as very small resistors, transistors and integrated circuits, where damage is likely as a result of overheating, a 25 watt iron is too large; a 12 to 15 watt type is preferred.

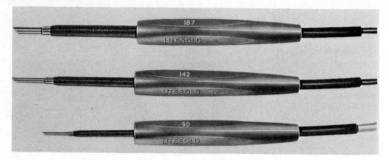

It is useful to have two soldering irons; one for printed circuit board work (12 or 15 W) and a larger one for tags and light metal work (20 to 25 W). A range of instruments is shown here; from top to bottom, 24 W, 20 W, and 12 W models. Other models within these two power ranges are available from other manufacturers (courtesy Light Soldering Developments Ltd.)

One should be able to make good electrical joints, which means that sufficient heat must be available to melt the solder and cause it to flow readily over the whole metallic surface being soldered. If this surface is not clean and free from oxidation or tarnish, the solder will not adhere to it; consequently a 'dry' joint is likely to result and a good electrical connection will not be achieved. If the mass of metal being joined is so great that quick solder flow does not occur, or perhaps the solder on the joint remains in a semi-tacky state while the hot iron is in contact, then a larger iron must be used. Of course, it is important to be careful of delicate components in this situation; the hotter iron must be used quickly and it is a good precaution to hold the wire of a delicate component with the wiring pliers so that some of the heat may be shunted away from the component.

Soldering irons are potentially dangerous instruments if they are not treated with care and respect. Because of the mains supply system used in the UK and in some other countries, soldering irons are required to be wired so that the bit and any other metal casing is connected to earth. If the bit comes into contact with a high voltage line, then the return current path will be back to earth, not via the person holding the iron. Because of this safety requirement, the British Home Office department has outlawed the sale of imported soldering irons that do not comply with this practice.

4

However, there could be an undesirable side effect of an earth connected iron when used on live equipment. There may exist in some equipment a small eddy current in the earth wiring (often experienced and reproduced as a hum in audio equipment) which may not cause problems in the normal course of events, but could be sufficient to cause damage to semiconductor devices if this current were inadvertently diverted via a base-emitter junction. This would be possible if, in these circumstances, an earthed soldering iron were allowed to touch

A multimeter having a sensitivity of at least 20,000 ohms per volt will serve most purposes of the constructor. This example is 40,000 ohms per volt and can be used with a high voltage probe attachment to measure up to 30kV (courtesy Chinaglia (UK) Ltd.)

the base connection of the semiconductor. The problem becomes more acute in circuits employing field-effect devices, which are even more sensitive to stray currents. If this situation is to be experienced by the constructor, then the soldering iron must be temporarily disconnected

5

from the supply and certainly unearthed while such a joint is made. It is probably best to isolate the equipment from the supply as well.

This particular problem and other safety factors can often be overcome by using low-voltage soldering irons that are powered by a car battery or driven via a low-voltage isolating transformer from the mains supply.

The soldering iron should always be placed in a fully protective stand when not in use—not suspended by means of a hook on a bench nail or equipment chassis. Exposed bits can burn clothing and are capable of causing severe burns to the skin. Do not leave the connecting lead trailing on the floor, especially where someone might trip on it and pull it from its mounting. One other precaution is in the use of soldering irons and often neglected until it is too late. Because of the use of artificial fibres in clothing, it is easy to sustain damage to it by melting. Stray splashes of hot solder and even spitting flux that lands on such clothing, especially trousers, will leave small holes on them, caused by melting. Place a protective sheet or cotton rag over your clothes, or better still wear a properly fitting work coat, that covers your thighs.

From time to time the iron will probably go black due to oxidation of the copper. If the tip is not kept scrupulously clean and properly tinned (coated evenly with solder) it cannot be expected to make a good joint. When you have several hundreds of joints to carry out, one bad one will cause trouble and will take a very long time to locate. It is always worthwhile to keep the job and the iron in good clean condition. If the bit becomes pitted or eroded into a concave shape at the tip, it should be cleaned and reshaped with a flat face by filing with a fine flat file. Then retinning should be carried out by melting solder on the tip and wiping away the surplus with a damp sponge or rag. It is a good idea to keep this sponge or rag handy to wipe away any other surplus solder or debris from the bit during the course of your work.

Solder for work on electronic circuitry must contain a resin-based non-corrosive core suitable for this work; soft-soldering types of flux additives are not suitable as they may contain substances that could cause corrosion to the copper wire or tag. The most popular size is 18 s.w.g. because it will feed sufficient for each joint at one time without difficulty in manipulation, while still being capable of being applied in small or difficult situations. If is sufficiently stiff and flexible for most applications. Where a small or slow rate of feed to the joint is preferred, the constructor may find it easy to use a thinner solder of about 20 or 22 s.w.g. Solder packs are sold in different sizes and, of course, the larger size is usually the most economic in the long run. Handy dispenser tubes are available, but one should always bear in mind that you pay for the dispenser as well as the solder, so it may seem to be a more expensive proposition. Unfortunately, some manufacturers do not state on some solder packs how much there is inside, so it is seldom possible to ascertain the real value for money aspect without buying them all and analysing them.

Other Basic Requirements

The tools mentioned here are the minimum needed to start practical work on electronic equipment. It will soon become apparent that these are not sufficient and one should expect to add to them as the need arises. Additional items that are likely to be wanted at some stage or other will include a couple of screwdrivers (3 and 6 mm blade width) spanners to fit BA and/or metric nuts and one for potentiometer nuts (13 mm A/F). Others that can be purchased later may include wire strippers, although wire cutters can, with care, be used in this dual role, cross-head (Philips or Pozidriv) screwdriver, hand drill with a selection

Modular construction technique. The circuits are built up on plug-in printed circuit boards. This photo shows a system of boards specially designed for logic integrated circuits, such as described in Chapter 6 (courtesy Critchley Bros. Ltd.)

of small twist drill bits to suit BA and/or small metric bolts and self-tapping screws. Guidance is given in the Appendix on the sizes of the most commonly used screws.

7

The best equipped workshop will also be stocked with a range of wire which will include solid core and multi-strand flexible p.v.c. wire for small interconnections and wiring looms; these can be obtained in a variety of different colours which should be used where possible to help identification. Other wire often forgotten but frequently required will be the bare tinned copper type about 20 or 22 s.w.g. and some plastic sleeving 1.5 mm, 3 mm and possibly 5 mm. Cables can be purchased as required because of their special purposes and would probably include single-core screened, low-loss coaxial, twin screened, three-core mains, and multi-way cables.

A variety of hardware will be required, including small nuts, bolts and washers in various sizes, the most common being 2BA, 4BA, 6BA and a selection of self-tapping screws of similar sizes. Soldering tags for fitting to 4BA and 6BA bolts, cable cleats, ties and lacing cord, grommets for fitting to ¼, ³/₈ and ½ inch holes, and a variety of tag strips are all useful items to accumulate. Others will be required in due course and can be added to the stock, in most cases being bought in quantities larger than the immediate needs. Table 1 shows some of the more common requirements and their details to help in the quick selection of items to buy and to assist when used in practical project work. Baseboards of various types can be stocked but it would be a costly exercise at the beginning when buying the early necessities. It is always a good idea to obtain catalogues from components suppliers, especially those that provide extra information on the characteristics or properties of the items that are offered. Some suppliers even provide a service of applications information which is an excellent way of acquiring product details.

Table 1. Basic workshop requirements

Tools
Soldering iron 15 watt for p.c.b. work
                    25 watt for heavier work
Wire cutters with insulated handles 5-6 in (125-150 mm)
Wiring pliers, long-nosed 6-7 in (150-180 mm)
Screwdrivers 3/32 in (2.5 mm) for skeleton preset controls
                    1/8 in (3 mm) for small screws
                    3/16 in (5 mm) long bladed for most slotted screws
                    Cross-head type, small for Philips screws
Solder 60/40 or similar resin-cored 18 s.w.g.
Connecting wire, solid single core 1 x 0.6 mm, insulated
                    flexible single core 7 x 0.20mm, insulated
                    twin flexible, 2 colours
                    mains cable, 3-core 13 x 0.20 mm
Nuts, bolts and washers, 2BA, 4BA, 6BA, 8BA.
Construction base, such as perforated s.r.b.p. or copper stripboard.
Multirange meter will be an early requirement and should not be a cheap one with limited ranges. Sensitivity at least 20 kΩ/volt

2 Resistors and potentiometers

Resistance of an electrical conductor is that property which restricts current flow. All metals and some non-metallic minerals are able to conduct electricity; they are equally able, to some degree, to control current flow due to their inherent properties of resistivity. Whilst not intending to present a learned thesis on the theory of electrons, it is useful to be able to have an understanding of the basis on which resistance is derived since it will answer some of the questions arising on resistive components.

Each different kind of element that will conduct has an inherent property, based on the its atomic structure, that determines its resistivity, that is its ability to oppose current flow. Resistivity is the constant factor that is measured in terms of resistance of a material per given volume. Hence it is usually expressed as the resistance in micro-ohms multiplied by the cross-sectional area, divided by the length. If

Table 2. Resistivity of some common materials. These figures are based on units of resistivity of micro-ohm-cm at 0°C

Silver	1.4
Copper	1.6
Aluminium	2.6
Gold	2.2
Iron	8.9
Platinum	9.8
Lead	19.8
Carbon	> 800 (varies according to density)

the material is subjected to heat or sub-zero temperature, its resistance will change; this is particularly noticeable in electronics when a fault condition occurs involving the overheating of components. In some

9

cases the resistive properties may revert to normal, but if the overheating is prolonged, permanent damage is likely to result.

It will soon be appreciated that electronic components are designed and made to take advantage of the inherent resistivity of a given material in conjunction with its other properties. As an example, it is a well known fact that copper is one of the lowest resistance materials there is; that is why it is used for making wire. In recent years aluminium has been adopted for special applications where tensile strength is important. At the other end of the scale, carbon is a highly resistive material, so it is widely used in making resistors and potentiometers. The resistivities of the most commonly used materials in electronics are given in Table 2 and these figures are based on measurements at $0^{\circ}C$ for a cubic centimetre of the material stated. The resistance is calculated as

$$R = \frac{\text{resistivity x length}}{\text{cross-sectional area}} \text{ ohms}$$

Table 3. Resistance colour coding and value coding

Colour	Band 1 1st digit	Band 2 2nd digit	Band 3 Multiplier	Multiplier value code example
Gold	—	—	0.1	R33 = 0.33Ω
Black	no digit.	0	1	3R3 = 3.3Ω 3E3
Brown	1	1	10	33R = 33Ω 33E
Red	2	2	100	330R = 330Ω 330E
Orange	3	3	1 000	3k3 = 3.3k = 3300Ω
Yellow	4	4	10 000	33k = 33 000Ω
Green	5	5	100 000	330k = 330000Ω
Blue	6	6	1 000 000	3M3=3.3M = 3 300 000Ω
Violet	7	7	10 million	33M = 33 million Ω
Grey	8	8	100 million	330M = 330 million Ω
White	9	9	1 000 million	

From this, we can determine the current flow in the material when subjected to an electromotive force of one volt applied to its extreme ends, which will be one ampere for a total resistance of one ohm.

Notice that the figure for carbon is only an approximation because it can be compressed into a given volume, so resulting in a predetermined density and, hence, resistivity. Consequently its resistance can be controlled during a manufacturing process, either by compression or by a combination of compression and mixing with other materials.

Table 3a. Tolerance ratings based on a permitted deviation from the nominal value by a percentage of it

Band 4 Colour	Band 5 Colour	Tolerance percentage	Tolerance letter code
—	—	0.1	B
—	—	0.25	C
—	—	0.5	D
Brown	—	1.0	F
Red	—	2.0	G
Gold	—	5.0	J
Silver	—	10.0	K
*No colour	—	20.0	M
—	—	30.0	N
—	+ Pink	Grade 1 high stability	

* This only applies where there are three colour bands only over the normal body colour

+This only applies where there are four other colour bands or where the value is written on a pink coloured body.

Although seldom used in electronics construction, it is worth mentioning that the conductivity of a material is determined by the opposite effect of resistivity. Therefore, it is logical to call the unit for conductivity the 'mho', which is the reciprocal of the resistivity (now often

11

expressed in Siemens). It is easy to see that the lowest resistivity represents the highest conductivity.

For a number of years the manufacture of resistors has been largely concentrated on compressed carbon rod types because of their simplicity, but experience in advancing technology, and in particular with current critical tolerance and stability requirements, the carbon rod is no longer considered to be either economical or possessing optimum performance characteristics. Over the past two years or so it has gradually been phased out of production and replaced by modern improved alternatives. However, since it will be found in equipment still in use for some time, it is useful to be able to recognise it and distinguish it from other types. The very old versions were crude carbon rods with wrapped wire ends and painted to a colour code based on that given in Table 3, in which the body colour denotes the first digit, the tip colour the second digit and the spot in the middle of its length is the multiplier. A gold or silver splash of paint at the opposite end denotes the tolerance of 5 or 10% respectively. Later types used in the last 25 years or so have been made with a protective porcelain or ceramic coating, so that the carbon composition could not be easily damaged, so altering its resistance. In fact, with the old unprotected types, it was common practice to file them to adjust the resistance value. Table 3a shows the code for tolerance.

The coated types were made in three common sizes and rated at 1/4 W, 1/2 W, and 1 W, while a 2 W version was introduced very much later. Due to the demand for small components for fitting into confined areas, such as in military equipment, it became necessary to introduce a smaller resistor rated at 1/8 W. Subsequent improvements in manufacturing technique resulted in this range of resistors being up-graded to 1/4 W and a 3/4 W version was also introduced.

The main limitation of these resistors is that they may become 'noisy' with age and tend to deviate from the nominal value by more than some circuits will accept. A high-stability type was developed, although more expensive, which could be made with a closer tolerance rating and higher noise immunity. These are still being made today and are based on the controlled processing of the carbon composition in a spiral track around a ceramic former.

Today the range of fixed value resistors is much greater because the advances in mineral technology has meant that much closer control on manufacturing tolerance can be achieved at an economic cost. It has also meant that smaller resistors can be made, some of them using controlled doping techniques as in semiconductor devices and integrated circuits. The inclusion of resistive elements in integrated circuits

12

was thought to have a serious effect on the requirement for discrete resistors, but this has not proved to be the case in practice. The demand for resistors is much higher now than ever and at one time the manufacturers were hard pressed to keep up with the demand. Among those currently available are the carbon film types previously mentioned, metal film and metal oxide, moulded carbon composition, thick film 'cermet' type, and wirewound.

The carbon film types available today are made by depositing a homogeneous film of carbon material on a ceramic body and cutting a spiral in the surface to achieve the required resistance value. These are then coated with a thick protective layer of insulating substance to exclude environmental influences. Colour coding bands are printed on the body in the conventional way according to the standard colour code given in Table 3. These are usually made in sizes ranging from 0.1 W to 2 W with tolerances of 2, 5, and 10%.

Metal film resistors offer high factors of stability, noise immunity, and variation due to temperature. They are made by depositing a metallic alloy in a similar manner to the carbon film type. Their advantage is in the low tolerance, generally intended for precision equipment. The temperature coefficient and noise level are also lower, and their resistance to the effects of heat from soldering is improved. These types are usually marked with their values in a number code, similar to that given in Table 3, and are larger than the carbon types.

Metal oxide types are similar in appearance to colour coded carbon film types, but they have characteristics similar to those of the metal film group. Both metal oxide and metal film types are more expensive than the carbon types, the metal being an alloy of tin.

Thick film 'cermet' types are much smaller than the carbon or metal types above for a comparative power rating. The ½ W version is generally about two-thirds the size, has a low temperature coefficient and is otherwise comparable in performance with the metal oxide type. Larger thick film resistors rated at 2 W are made to withstand up to 15 kV and are about 53 mm body length.

Wirewound resistors vary a great deal in both size and shape but all have the same basic characteristics. Points to remember are that they are usually used in power circuits so they will dissipate a fair amount of heat. Because of this, they should not be used where the stability is of importance. They are invariably made by winding resistance wire on to a ceramic former and given a coating of fixing cement to maintain the position of the wire. Resistance values range from a fraction of an ohm up to about 10 kilohms; occasionally higher values may be found, but these are not common. The temperature coefficient is low and tolerances are mostly 5%, although because of manufacturing difficulties those below one ohm may have a 10% tolerance. Power ratings are high making them particularly suitable for use as voltage droppers in power supplies, the most common being 2½, 5, and 10 W. Some of the more expensive types have a vitreous coating, usually green

Fig. 1. Fixed resistors

Fig. 1a. Carbon rod resistors are usually cylindrical in shape and have protective coatings

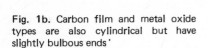

Fig. 1b. Carbon film and metal oxide types are also cylindrical but have slightly bulbous ends'

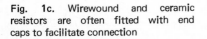

Fig. 1c. Wirewound and ceramic resistors are often fitted with end caps to facilitate connection

Fig. 1d. Vitreous wirewound resistors have an extra tough coating usually coloured green

Fig. 1e. Tapped wirewound resistors used as voltage droppers in power supplies have connection straps at each end and part of the way along the tubular former

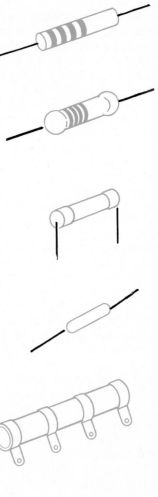

Fig. 1. Fixed resistors

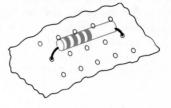

Fig. 1f. Low-power carbon resistors are mounted close to the circuit board

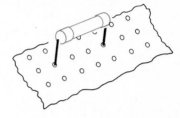

Fig. 1g. Higher power wirewound resistors that dissipate appreciable heat should be mounted well clear of the circuit board to encourage air circulation

in colour. The resistance and tolerance values in most cases are hand-written on the body.

The general appearance of various types of resistor is shown in Fig. 1.

It is almost impossible to generalise on the maximum voltage that one should apply to resistors because it varies so much from one type to another and from one manufacturer to another. This is particularly the case with precision or high-stability types, but as a very approximate guide Table 5 gives an indication of what to expect. Constructors who have particular problems are recommended to consult the manufacturer's data. Table 5 has been compiled on the basis of carbon types; it is possible that these ratings may be exceeded with care within the recommended figures. The short burst column is based on application of a pulse of less than one second duration. It should be remembered that the higher the resistance the lower will be the recommended current or voltage rating. The figures for power are nominal ratings derived from the d.c. formula $P = I^2R = P^2/R$, at $70°C$.

Tolerance figures for nominal resistance values from 1.0 to 9.1 ohms are given in Table 6. These have been calculated on the basis of 1, 2, 5, 10 and 20% tolerances and show the maximum range above and below the nominal value. For higher resistance the figures must be multiplied by the appropriate factor, for example, 3.3 kilohms at 5% will have a tolerance limit of 165 ohms above and below 3300. The resistance values given in the left-hand column are the nominal

15

preferred value series applicable according to the manufacturers' ranges. Not all values are included in all of these ranges. For the full value ranges, see Table 4.

The colour coding, given in Table 3 and Fig. 2, also includes the current form of coding used on resistors with the value marked in number and letter code. Notice that the use of R and E (right-hand

Table 4. Standard resistor values in ranges to BS 2488 (IEC 63)

Digits		*E24 Range (2 and 5% tol)*				*E12 Range (5 and 10% tol)*				*E6 Range (20% tol)*			
1st	*2nd*	*+M*	*Blk*	*Red*	*Yell*	*+M*	*Blk*	*Red*	*Yell*	*+M*	*Blk*	*Red*	*Yell*
Brn	Blk	10	Ik	100k		10	1k	100k		10	1k	100k	
Brn	Brn	11	1·1k	↓									
Brn	Red	12	1·2k			12	1·2k	120k					
Brn	Or	13	1·3k										
Brn	Grn	15	1·5k			15	1·5k	150k		15	1·5k	150k	
Brn	Blue	16	1·6k										
Brn	Grey	18	1·8k			18	1·8k	180k					
Red	Blk	20	2·0k										
Red	Red	22	2·2k			22	2·2k	220k		22	2·2k	220k	
Red	Yell	24	2·4k										
Red	Vi	27	2·7k			27	2·7k	270k					
Or	Blk	30	3·0k										
Or	Or	33	3·3k	All values		33	3·3k	330k		33	3·3k	330k	
Or	Blue	36	3·6k										
Or	Wh	39	3·9k			39	3·9k	390k					
Yell	Or	43	4·3k										
Yell	Vi	47	4·7k			47	4·7k			47	4·7k	470k	
Grn	Brn	51	5·1k										
Grn	Blue	56	5·6k			56	5·6k	560k					
Blue	Red	62	6·2k										
Blue	Grey	68	6·8k			68	6·8k	680k		58	6·8k	680k	
Vi	Grn	75	7·5k					↓					
Grey	Red	82	8·2k	↓		82	8·2k	820k					
Wh	Brn	91	9·1k	910k									
Brn	Blk	Brn 100	Or 10k	Grn 1M		Brn 100	Or 10k	Grn 1M		Brn 100	Or 10k	Grn 1M	
		↓	↓			↓	↓	↓		↓		↓	
		910	91k			820	82k	8·2M		680	6·8k	8·2M	
								Blue 10M				Blue 10M	

Table 5. Preferred values of resistors in standard ranges and tolerance

Resistance (ohms)	Tolerance value of deviation from nominal rating				
	± 1%	± 2%	± 5%	± 10%	± 20%
1.0	0.01	0.02	0.05	0.1	0.2
1.1	0.011	0.022	0.055	0.11	0.22
1.2	0.012	0.024	0.06	0.12	0.24
1.5	0.015	0.03	0.075	0.15	0.30
1.8	0.018	0.036	0.090	0.18	0.36
2.0	0.02	0.04	0.10	0.20	0.40
2.2	0.022	0.044	0.11	0.22	0.44
2.4	0.024	0.048	0.12	0:24	0.48
2.7	0.027	0.054	0.135	0.27	0.54
3.0	0.030	0.060	0.150	0.30	0.60
3.3	0.033	0.066	0.165	0.33	0.66
3.6	0.036	0.072	0.180	0.36	0.72
3.9	0.039	0.078	0.195	0.39	0.78
4.3	0.043	0.086	0.215	0.43	0.86
4.7	0.047	0.094	0.235	0.47	0.94
5.1	0.051	0.102	0.255	0.51	1.02
5.6	0.056	0.112	0.280	0.56	1.12
6.2	0.062	0.124	0.310	0.62	1.24
6.8	0.068	0.136	0.340	0.68	1.36
7.5	0.075	0.150	0.375	0.75	1.50
8.2	0.082	0.164	0.410	0.82	1.64
9.1	0.091	0.182	0.455	0.91	1.82

The appropriate multiplier factor should be taken into account

column) are synonymous and may appear on different manufacturers' products. Many a rhyme has been devised to help remember the colour code sequence; among them is the following that readers may like to adopt:

Bye Bye Rosie, Off You Go, Birmingham Via Great Western. Black Brown Red Orange Yellow Green Blue Violet Grey White.

In Table 3a the tolerance code is given and this may not be so easy to remember. Until fairly recently, the most familiar were the gold 5% and the silver 10% values. Now we have a much wider range

17

that uses brown and red from the conventional colour code system, plus a few others. Consequently it has become necessary to introduce the letter coding as shown in the right-hand column, which would appear on hand written resistors immediately after the resistance value, for example 3k3J indicates a resistance nominal value of 3300 within a 5% tolerance rating. Some high-grade resistors have a pink body or a fifth colour band in pink which indicates a particularly selected Grade 1 resistor for special applications requiring ultra-high stability in varying environmental conditions.

Physical sizes can vary between different types of resistor; Table 7 shows only a rough indication of relative sizes for carbon or metal oxide, wirewound and cermet type thick film resistors. These should be taken only as an approximation and exceptions may occur in occasional instances. The column of minimum hole space figures indicate how far

Fig. 2. Colour code

Fig. 2a. Resistance values and tolerance ratings are marked with a colour code; identification commences from the colour nearest to the end. These examples show a 3.3Ω 5% tolerance resistor

Fig. 2b. Alternative markings are shown with figures and letter multiplier codes. The last letter indicates the tolerance

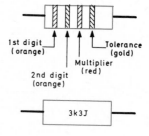

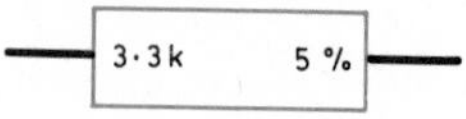

Fig. 2c. The easiest form of identification handwritten on the body

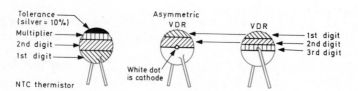

Fig. 2d. Nominal value codes for a negative coefficient thermistor, an asymmetric voltage dependent resistor, and other v.d.r.s

Table 6. Power ratings of carbon resistors. These figures are for guidance only; refer to manufacturer's data

Power rating (watts)	Suggested maximum applied voltage	
	Continuous d.c. volts or a.c. r.m.s.	Short burst d.c. or a.c. r.m.s.
0.1	125	200
0.125	150	250
0.25	200	400
0.5	350	650
1.0	500	800
2.0	700	1 000

Table 7. Approximate comparative sizes of resistors

Approx. minimum hole spacing.	Approx. body length,	Approx. comparative body size.	W at 70°C type metal oxide or carbon.
8 mm (0.3 in)	4 to 5 mm		0.125 W
12 mm (0.5 in)	7 to 9 mm		0.25 W
14 mm (0.6 in)	9 to 11 mm		0.5 W
23 mm (0.9 in)	15 to 18 mm		1.0 W
26 mm (1.0 in)	18 to 24 mm		2.0 W
19 mm (0.8 in)	13 to 15 mm		Wirewound 2.5
14 mm (0.6 in)	20 to 25 mm		5
50 mm (2 in)	40 to 55 mm		10
10 mm (0.4 in)	7 mm		Thick film cermet type 0.5 W

The body size rectangles are here shown approximately half full size.

apart fixing holes may need to be in perforated or printed circuit board. This is based on the sizes indicated in the third column.

Since the values of resistance, voltage and current are inter-related by Ohm's law (Fig. 3) we can derive these values from the formula $R = V/I$ for both d.c. and a.c. circuits (provided that there are no phase shift factors in an a.c. circuit). Fig. 4a shows a simple circuit which

19

consists of a battery supplying V volts to a resistance R1; the current is shown as I. In this circuit the resistance in ohms will be equal to V volts ÷ I amperes. In electronics we seldom have to deal with such

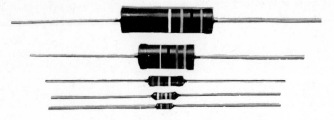

Comparative sizes of typical carbon film resistors; from top to bottom these are 2 W, 1 W, 1/2 W, 1/3 W, 1/4 W types

Fig. 3.

Graph showing the relationship between voltage, current and resistance for four resistance values

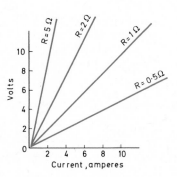

large units as amperes except in power circuits, so it is useful to remember that this formula is exactly the same as saying the resistance in kilohms is equal to V volts ÷ I milliamperes. One kilohm = 1 000 ohms and one milliampere = 1/1 000 ampere.

A circuit combining two resistors in series is shown in Fig. 4b and the same formulae apply. The total resistance must be found first by adding the values of the two separate resistors. Similarly in Fig. 4c the three resistor values must be added together to be able use the formula.

If two resistors are connected in parallel as shown in Fig. 4d then the combined resistance is equal to

$$R_{\text{tot}} = \frac{R_1 \times R_2}{R_1 + R_2} \quad \text{ohms}$$

20

In Fig. 4e the combined resistance is equal to

$$R_{tot} = \frac{R_1 \times R_2 \times R_3}{(R_1 \times R_2) + (R_2 \times R_3) + (R_3 \times R_1)} \quad \text{ohms}$$

These two formulae are very much easier to handle than the equivalent reciprocal resistance formula often found in textbooks, although they may not be so easy to remember.

Fig. 4. Series and parallel resistors

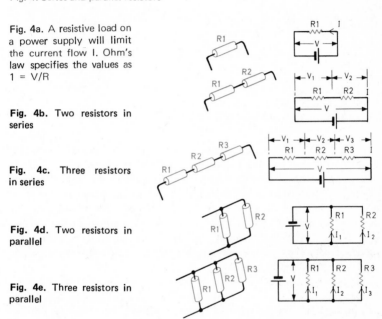

Fig. 4a. A resistive load on a power supply will limit the current flow I. Ohm's law specifies the values as 1 = V/R

Fig. 4b. Two resistors in series

Fig. 4c. Three resistors in series

Fig. 4d. Two resistors in parallel

Fig. 4e. Three resistors in parallel

The graph that illustrates the formula for Ohm's law is shown in Fig. 3. From this it will be observed that the law is a linear one that is represented by a straight line, in this particular illustration the line being representative of the resistance. One can make up a composite chart incorporating the scale values of voltage and current for given values of resistance, simply by drawing a straight line through the zero datum and the single plot determined by calculation for one set of

21

values. All relevant voltage and current values can then be read off from this graph.

If two resistors are connected in a potential divider form as shown in Fig. 5a, then calculations become more complicated by the introduction of two current paths; from A to B and from A to C via B. In order to calculate these currents the terminals BC must either be considered

Fig. 5a. (left). The effective circuit of a potential divider
Fig. 5b. (right). The equivalent circuit using fixed resistors in place of a potentiometer

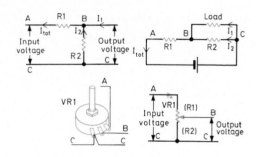

Fig. 5c. A potentiometer can be used as a variable potential divider network

as having a load R2 or must be connected to an external load across the output, in which case the load resistance must be combined in parallel with R2 and this combination will be in series with R1. The individual currents will be determined by the formulae given above in the normal way. Fig. 5b shows the equivalent circuit that could apply here for the purposes of the calculation. The equivalent is a potentiometer which is also shown; the sliding wiper has the choice of position within the range of overall resistance so that the voltage or current through the load can be pre-selected.

Potentiometers are usually recognisable as controls with knobs or presettable screwdriver slots, so that a d.c. voltage or a.c. signal can be adjusted, for example, a volume control. The principles are the same, although rarely does anyone need to go to the extent of calculating exactly the current and voltages under various situations of the wiper setting. It is by experience in the practice of electronics that potentiometer values are determined according to the application, bearing in mind the possible effects of shunting a high impedance source or risking excessive current flow when the control is at one end of its travel. There are often known values that are adopted by convention for various applications and these will become familiar to the constructor.

22

It has been for a long time the convention to arrange the carbon or wirewound tracks of potentiometers in a circular form so that the controls can be rotated and the whole component contained in a fairly small space economically. However, there is a growing trend in domestic equipment to adopt the style used for a number of years in studios, whereby the track is straight and the moving wiper is arranged to travel in a straight line. There are no rules or factors that dictate which method is adopted; it is largely a question of aesthetics or personal whim.

A range of rotary type potentiometers that are representative of generally available styles. From left to right, spindle carbon track type with a flat for helping the knob screw to grip; short spindle type wirewound control for precision instruments; carbon track skeleton preset types for printed circuit board mounting; cermet trimmers with screwdriver slot control

The main groups of potentiometers are classified in two parts: those called linear and those called log types. The difference is in the moulding or composition of the track, whereby the change of resistance with the movement of the wiper is either by uniform amounts throughout the length of the track (linear), or where the change of resistance per uniform movement of the wiper is on a non-linear basis, that is, either in increasing or decreasing (logarithmic) increments. Examples of graphs showing the difference between these are shown in Fig. 6. The majority of non-linear scales follow a logarithmic law of increment so that when rotated clockwise, the wiper picks off an increasing increment. This is easily illustrated by reference to the common volume control. Starting from a fully counter-clockwise position and rotating

23

clockwise, the voltage at the wiper will increase slowly to start with, then more quickly as rotation proceeds. The reason for using log

A range of slider track type potentiometers. From left to right, single track slider control; helical worm geared preset types with very fine control, usually of the cermet type. Below, a group picture of helical potentiometers and sliders. (All these photos by courtesy of Egen Electric Limited)

Fig. 6. Potentiometers

The graphical representation of the linear taper and logarithmic laws of progression of resistance for clockwise rotation of potentiometers

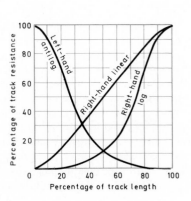

potentiometers (usually abbreviated to 'pot') is to counterbalance the logarithmic scale of frequency versus pitch of audio and high frequency signals, to provide a better degree of control on normal listening levels and to control h.f. and r.f. signals in a similar manner during processing. It is possible to obtain potentiometers for special applications where an anti-log law is required, such as in connection with thermistor controls.

One other type is the linear taper pot in which the increment changes in a linear fashion as opposed to a non-linear or log type. The graph of a typical example is shown in Fig. 6.

Apart from these two or three classifications, potentiometers are made in enclosed style with a control spindle or open style called 'skeleton presets' (Fig. 7). The latter are generally of a low power rating (less than one watt and as low as 0.1 W) and made as a vertical or horizontal mounting for printed circuit or similar boards. They usually have linear tracks, with an angle of rotation of between 200° and 270°. Contact between the wiper and the track is either by direct metal spring or carbon brush. both being open to the accumulation of dirt, grease or debris which will cause fault conditions to occur at some time. To alleviate this problem, there is increasing use of similar small pots that are enclosed within a plastic case. Because the track is very thin, it is likely to wear quickly and increase the risk of noisy operation and/or intermittent open circuit. Although these disadvantages may deter the potential user, the very low cost of these items does not seem to discourage their widespread use. Of course, where there is a risk of stray pick-up from nearby signal carriers, they should be replaced by enclosed screened types. Alternative cermet preset pots can be used where dirt is a problem, but they are much more expensive. It is up to the constructor to decide on the long term cost effectiveness in his choice.

Cermet types are known to have favourable low noise and high stability. They can also be obtained in the form of a 'rectilinear' pot which comprises a helical screw multi-turn adjustment linked to a straight line travelling wiper. For precision control and minute increments, this pot is ideal; some of them have extremely good long term stability, rated up to one watt.

Potentiometers designed for spindle control are available in log or linear form, with or without on-off switches, and can be obtained as two controls ganged together for common knob operation, specially for twin channel or stereo equipment. They are larger then their preset counterparts and have carbon composition tracks. Wirewound types are all linear and generally of the lower resistance values up to about 100kΩ. They have a higher power rating then carbon types, up to 3 W

25

in most cases, while some older versions are 5 W. Angle of rotation of all spindle pots ranges between 260° and 320°, although the effective electrical scale is often slightly less than the full extent of mechanical rotation angle. Wirewound pots are not available with switches.

Fig. 7. Potentiometers

Fig. 7a. Physical proportions of a common size potentiometer such as is used for volume and tone controls. Spindle sizes may be 1/4 in (6.4 mm) or Continental 6 mm. Both sizes are adopted for knobs, so check first

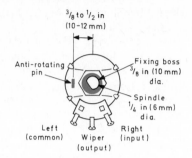

Fig. 7b. A typical skeleton preset potentiometer for printed circuit board mounting

Fig. 7c. An enclosed cermet type preset potentiometer for printed circuit board mounting

Fig. 7d. A slider type control without the knob, such as used for volume and signal level controls

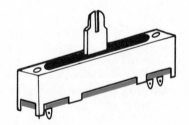

26

Carbon types with spindles are rated from 0.05 W for the sub-miniature types, while the larger standard size is rated at 1 W for log types and 2 W for linear types, this difference being common in most cases. Switches that are ganged to the potentiometer are usually intended for mains operation at ratings up to 250 V 2A a.c., which should be sufficient to control the mains supply to almost any colour television set or record reproduction system.

Table 8. Power ratings of potentiometers. These figures are for guidance only; refer to manufacturers' data. Cermet types are rated at lower voltages in some cases

Power rating (watts) at 70°C	Suggested maximum applied voltage	
	Continuous d.c. or a.c. r.m.s.	Short burst
0.1	125	150
0.25	150	250
0.40	200 to 300	350
0.50	200 to 350	500
0.75	250 to 400	500
1.0	350 to 500	600
2.0	400 to 600	750

The resistance values of potentiometers have not, so far, been aligned with the standard preferred value range of fixed resistors, but it is possible that this could happen sometime in the future. Suggested voltages for given power ratings are shown in Table 8, but should be taken only as a rough guide because the real value will depend on individual types and the applications; refer to manufacturers' data for a more accurate guide.

Of increasing popularity is the 'slider' potentiometer in which the track is straight and the variable control is by means of a knob that can be moved in a straight line. This particular type is often found on audio equipment because it has the advantage of being easier to use with a calibrated scale. Those generally available to the constructor are small (about 2½ in or 100 mm long) while the precision types that are used on consoles in television and sound studios are about twice the size and fitted with a calibrated scale.

Those used by constructors, usually costing less than a pound each, are available in a wide range of resistance values from about 10 kilohms to 2 megohms, covering almost all needs for control panels. Power ratings are usually from ¼ to ½ W, the higher power rating being for linear types. They can be obtained in single or twin (stereo) track versions, the latter having a screen between the two tracks. It is often the case that the plastic or other knob is supplied as a separate item,

Fig. 8. Thermistors

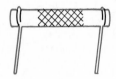

Fig. 8a. Rod type thermistor with negative temperature coefficient

Fig. 8b. Disc type thermistor

Fig. 8c. Glass bead thermistors

Fig. 8d. End capped rod thermistor

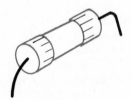

so one should make sure of ordering both; in the case of the stereo version, two knobs are replaced by a single ganged control knob.

Rectilinear potentiometers are similar in principle to the slider type except that control is preset by means of a screwdriver slotted helical worm drive. These are available as wirewound or cermet trimmers and mostly fitted with pins for mounting on printed circuit

Fig. 9. V.D.R.

Disc type voltage dependent resistor otherwise known as a Varistor

boards. The resistance range is from 10 ohms to about 500 kilohms and power ratings are from ½ to 1 W. They are smaller than the slider type — about ¾ to 1¼ in (19 to 32 mm) long. The cost of these types is high because of the mechanism employed, so this tends to make them prohibitive from the constructor's point of view.

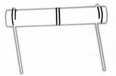

Fig. 10. Spark gaps

Spark gaps used in e.h.t. circuits, such as in television, allow the discharge of static charge build-up. The rod type (left) looks a bit like a rod thermistor with silver painted ends and a small gap in the centre; the larger ring type uses high temperature wire

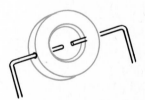

Other types of resistive device use properties of variability according to external influences (Fig. 8). These include thermistors; the negative temperature coefficient type (n.t.c.) raising its resistance when the ambient temperature falls, and *vice versa*. The cheapest are the rod types which are commonly used for voltage or current stabilisation or temperature monitoring. Glass bead types are more expensive and are used for temperature measurement. No obvious identification marks are likely to be shown and the constructor should not allow different types to be mixed.

Voltage-dependent resistors (Fig. 9) change their resistance according to the applied voltage and do have colour coded identification in some cases as in Fig. 2d. Fig. 10 shows two types of spark gap which should not be confused with resistors or thermistors.

3 Capacitors

Place two metallic plates close to each other and overlapping but not touching, and we have the basic capacitor—in theory at any rate. But there is much more to it than that. So many factors have become involved in modern capacitors to meet the increasingly stringent demands of industrial and military equipment that the constructor is confronted by the spin-off involving a large number of different types.

Traditionally, textbooks on the subject state that the capacitor is a means of storing an electric charge. This is true, but then it also has other purposes that depend on its subsidiary characteristics, such as its time factor in charging or discharging; its reactance when used in a.c. signal processing applications; its ability to affect frequency response when used with an inductor or resistor; its ability to block d.c. while appearing to present a short circuit or resistive circuit to a.c. Apart from these features, capacitors exhibit varying characteristics relating to stability, d.c. resistance (or insulation), tolerance and reliability, and voltage handling ability. This chapter will attempt to sort out many of the features that tend to cause confusion among constructors and highlight the differences between the various types. First, some more general notes that are applicable to most, if not all, types. It is worth studying or keeping for reference the illustrations and data given in the tables and charts so that they can be used as and when needed for a particular project.

Capacitance

The capacitance is measured as a unit, multiple or submultiple of the microfarad, this being equivalent to one millionth of a farad. Why use such a clumsy unit when farads are seldom if ever required at all? The

31

point really is that the farad was adopted and based on the very large capacitive storage effects that occur in power equipment. To bring this into the realms of relatively small electronic equipment, submultiples are needed. The appendix shows how multiples and submultiples are calculated and named according to the application. In the case of capacitors, the common terms are microfarad, picofarad and of more recent adoption nanofarad. Components are labelled as to their capacitance in various ways using any of these terms; it is important, therefore, to become familiar with the equivalent expressions of capacitance in any of these terms.

Table 9. Number and letter coding, multipliers and equivalents of capacitor values

	Capacitance value equivalents		
Capacitance code	pF picofarads	nF nanofarads	µF microfarads
1p0	1	0.001	0.000 001
10p	10	0. 01	0.000 01
100p	100	0.1	0.000 1
1n0	1 000	1.0	0.001
10n	10 000	10.0	0.01
100n	100 000	100.0	0.1
1u0	1 000 000	1 000	1.0
10u		10 000	10.0
100u		100 000	100.0
1000u		1 000 000	1 000.0

Table 9 summarises the equivalents of capacitance so that the constructor can see at a glance what the markings on the components mean, where they are hand-written or printed on them in figures and letters. Some capacitors are marked with a colour code, but unfortunately there are many variations in the way that this code is expressed and interpreted. To avoid likely confusion or incorrect deciphering of the code, Table 10 is given here to be used in conjunction with Fig. 11, which identifies the various methods so far known to the author and found in the UK.

32

Table 10. Colour coding of capacitance, tolerance, temperature coefficient and voltage of capacitors

Colour	1 1st digit pF	2 2nd digit pF	M Multiplier	T Tolerance <10pF	Tolerance >10pF	TC Temperature coefficient code	TC1 Temperature coefficient 1st digit	TCM Temperature coefficient multiplier	V Voltage ceramic, polyester	V Voltage tantalum
Black	0	0	1	±2pF	±20%	NPO (0×10^{-6})	±0	1		10
Brown	1	1	10	±0.1pF	±1%	N030/N033 (-30×10^{-6})	-3	10	100	-
Red	2	2	100	-	±2%	N080/N075 (-80×10^{-6})	-8	100	200 or 250	-
Orange	3	3	1 000	±0.25pF	±2.5%	N150 (-150×10^{-6})	-1.5	1 000	300	-
Yellow	4	4	10 000	-	-	N220 (220×10^{-6})	-2.2	10 000	400	6.3
Green	5	5		±0.5pF	±5%	N330 (-330×10^{-6})	-3.3	-	500	16
Blue	6	6		-	-	N470 (-470×10^{-6})	-4.7		600	-
Violet	7	7		-	-	N750 (-750×10^{-6})	-7.5		700	-
Grey	8	8	0.01	-	-	P030 ($+30 \times 10^{-6}$)	+3		800	25
White	9	9	0.01 Spot also indicates anode wire	±1pF	±10%	P100 ($+ 100 \times 10^{-6}$) (N = Neg. TC P = Pos. TC)	+1	-	900	3 pink 35

The colour code also contains information on the voltage rating. In all capacitors this voltage is the maximum recommended d.c. continuous voltage that should be applied to the capacitor in normal use. Where capacitors are designed or intended for specific a.c. power applications, an a.c. voltage might be quoted; if not, then one can assume that an equivalent d.c. voltage rating of at least three times would be needed for the job.

Fig. 11. Capacitor colour codes

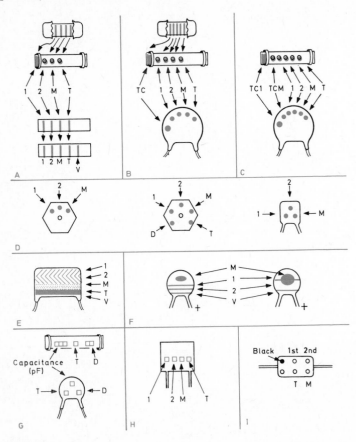

Colour coding of capacitors to be used in conjunction with Table 10. Ceramic types are shown in diagrams A to D, polyester at E and tantalum at F. Alternative coding is shown in G and H for figure and letter codes

34

As an example, where a 250 V a.c. capacitor would be used on mains supplies of 200 to 250 V a.c., one could, in theory replace this with a 750 V d.c. type. However, whilst the capacitor might withstand this applied voltage, it is recommended that the voltage rating should be increased to 1 000 V d.c. to allow for surge conditions at switch-on or high-voltage spike pulses caused by interference on the supply line.

Table 11. Capacitor dielectric constants at 25°C (approx.)

Air	1.0006
P.T.F.E.	2.0
Polystyrene	2.6
Polyethylene terephthalate*	3.2
Shellac	3.5
Dry paper	3.5
S.R.B.P.	4 to 5.5
Porcelain	5 to 6
Mica	5.4 to 8
Low-K ceramic	6 to 260
High-K ceramic	1 400 to 3 000
Electrolytic Aluminium oxide film	8.6
Tantalum oxide	>10

* Otherwise known as Melinex or polyester.

Whatever the voltage rating of a capacitor, the applied voltage can be any value less than this. If exceeded, then the insulation between the plates is liable to break down, causing sparking and possibly blowing a fuse or resulting in burning. Some suppliers quote both a.c. and d.c. voltage figures, which indicate more clearly that the capacitor can withstand both at voltages up to those quoted, even though they may not be in line with the factor of three described above.

Insulation and manufacturing methods play a significant role in determining the voltage characteristics, temperature range, stability and

35

storage life. Table 11 shows the more common of those insulation materials used, which are more correctly termed the 'dielectrics'. The size of the manufactured capacitor will also be determined by the choice of dielectric because the factor known as the dielectric constant will adjust the ultimate capacitance per unit area. This dielectric constant is a factor based on the capacitance of equivalent area of metal plate and separation in terms of an air space dielectric. Since air gives a factor of approximately one for the dielectric constant, all other insulating materials will give a comparatively larger capacitance. In Table 11 these factors are quoted and will give a guide to relative capacitance and, inversely, to size of component. However, one other feature is relevant and that is the thickness of the metal when the plates and dielectric film are rolled into a compact component.

Another feature of the dielectric that influences its application is its response in conjunction with the metal plates to environmental conditions and high frequencies. Since there is a phase difference between the voltage and current of an applied a.c. signal, the a.c. power factor of the capacitor is likely to be affected by changes in reactance at different frequencies.

Although not considered to be of great importance in most applications, it must be appreciated that the ability of the capacitor to behave in a predictable fashion is limited by this power factor and, hence, the effective frequency range of usefulness is limited by the dielectric. This is why certain types of capacitor are chosen for particular applications within their individual economic range. A wide variety of types can be interchanged in many general-purpose applications that are not critical of choice because of d.c. or low-frequency use. However, one also bears in mind the reliability and tolerance factors of one's choice in this respect. Size can be another consideration, especially where printed circuit layouts are contemplated.

With all these considerations to start with, how does one set about choosing the right type? Well, it is not easy to generalise and experience in studying specified components in particular circuits will show the constructor many of the usual practices. Later paragraphs will highlight some of the important features of individual types to help, but first let us look more closely at what one can do with capacitors.

In the previous chapter we saw how we could combine two or more resistors to obtain a joint resistance of different value. We can do similarly with capacitors, but in the inverse manner. Since capacitors have reactance, it follows that, at a given frequency we can combine two or more capacitors in series to obtain increased reactance by adding together the individual reactances. We can also combine two or more capacitors in parallel to obtain decreased values of reactance by adding the reciprocals of reactance, just as we did with resistors. However, since we do not recognise capacitors readily in reactance terms we need to translate this into equivalent capacitance terms. Reactance is inversely proportional to capacitance; therefore, using the formula

$$\text{Reactance} = \frac{1}{2 \pi f C}$$

we can draw up expressions for series and parallel capacitors in terms of capacitance, these being shown in Fig. 12. The combined effective

Fig. 12. Capacitors in parallel and series

Fig. 12a. Two capacitors connected in parallel to obtain a higher overall capacitance

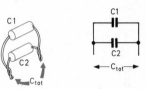

Fig. 12b. Two capacitors connected in series

capacitance of two or more in parallel is equal to the sum of the individual capacitances; the combined effective capacitance of two or more in series is not equal to the sum of the reciprocals of the individual capacitors, but found from the expression:

$$C_{\text{tot}} = \frac{C_1 \times C_2}{C_1 + C_2}$$

for two capacitors in series or

$$\frac{1}{C_{\text{tot}}} = \frac{1}{C_1} + \frac{1}{C_2} + \frac{1}{C_3} + \frac{1}{C_4} \ \ldots \text{etc}$$

for three or more capacitors in series.

Where capacitors are connected in parallel, the combined effective voltage rating is equivalent to that of the lowest in the group. Where capacitors are connected in series, the combined effective voltage rating is equivalent to the sum of the individual components' voltages.

Capacitors are often combined with either resistors or inductors in a circuit, so the combined effective resistance with reactance will determine the degree of a.c. voltage drop. Capacitors combined with inductors are outlined in the next chapter; here we can consider the effect of capacitors with resistors.

Fig. 13. CR circuits

Fig. 13a. A CR network to provide a simple high-pass filter, or to differentiate a square wave to produce a short pulse

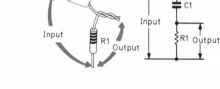

Fig. 13b. A CR network used to provide a low-pass filter

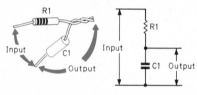

Fig. 13c. A T-filter used in a feedback circuit to provide bass boost

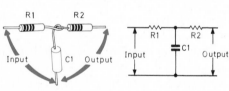

Fig. 13 shows the typical kinds of circuit used and the equivalents in resistive terms to a.c. Straight away, it can be seen that this is a form of potential divider and we can determine the effective output voltage for given input conditions. Since the frequency could vary, it follows that the reactance of the capacitor will change inversely, so altering the effective output voltage. For a wide range of frequencies the effective output does not change very significantly until the reactance of the capacitor is the same as the fixed resistance value. This is colloquially termed the 3 dB point since at this frequency the output voltage will be reduced to about 0.7 of the input voltage, equivalent to a loss of 3 dB.

38

As the frequency is progressively changed up or down according to whether it is a low-pass or high-pass network, the output will continue to fall at the rate of half of the preceding output per octave (or double frequency) increment or sub-octave (half frequency) decrement, respectively. Charts will show how to find these values quickly and are called 'nomograms'. From this information, one can predict frequency response or design tone controls or filters.

Capacitors are used in a similar manner with inductors to provide selective filtering over a narrow band of frequencies. Where these are of high frequency or r.f. the capacitor must be able to remain at a stable constant capacitance, so it is usual for ceramic or mica dielectric types to be used. These also come in a low tolerance rating, that is, the actual capacitance value is more likely to be near to the nominal value marked and certainly within the range indicated by the tolerance rating.

As explained in the previous chapter, tolerance implies that the capacitance is within a given percentage of deviation from the nominal. It does not mean that the capacitance of a particular sample will vary in itself. This tolerance does not apply to any other feature of the component.

Some typical examples of capacitor outlines in common use are shown in Figs. 11 and 14, although they are not drawn to scale because the size of each individual component varies according to the factors already described. They are briefly described in the following paragraphs, together with special features.

Ceramic

Ceramic capacitors are available in three basic styles: tubular, disc or plate, rod, or variations on any of these. This does not imply that one is any better than another for this reason, so the constructor will need to study performance characteristics to select for his needs. Generally, ceramic capacitors are very stable, and are ideal for h.f. and r.f. applications. Tolerance ratings are not very low.

Markings are shown in Fig. 11 and may appear in any of the styles shown except E and F. The colour code groups vary, so it is important to identify the style of coding used so as not to be mistaken in interpreting the code. Reading always starts from the left-hand end or, for tubular and rod types from the end which carries predominance of colour spots or bands. Body colour is not included as part of the code. Ceramic types are found in values ranging from a few picofarads to about 470 nF. Ceramic capacitors will also withstand high voltages; the very small types at 100V up to large disc types for several kilovolts. The voltage rating is not always clearly marked, so one should consult the suppliers or manufacturers' catalogue if in doubt. Size is generally small and, in particular, thin, so making them ideal for condensed layouts on printed circuit boards.

Fig. 14. Capacitors

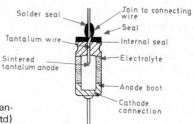

Solder seal
Tantalum wire
Sintered tantalum anode
Join to connecting wire
Seal
Internal seal
Electrolyte
Anode boot
Cathode connection

Fig. 14a. Sectional view of a wet tantalum capacitor (Courtesy Waycom Ltd)

Fig. 14b. A ceramic feed-through capacitor; this is normally fitted in a hole in a chassis plate or screen partition and has a very low capacitance

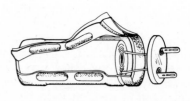

Fig. 14c. Cut-away views of dry electrolytic capacitors by Mullard: Wire-ended type is shown left and the tag type right

Electrolytic

Electrolytic capacitors rely for their full effectiveness on the application of a polarising d.c. voltage. They are inexpensive substitutes where large capacitance is required and space is limited. They were introduced as substitutes for the very large equivalent paper types that are more reliable over long-term conditions. The old electrolytic contains a paste and acts in a manner resembling a dry battery, except that its storage capacity is not as high and is incapable of supplying much power. Unlike the dry battery, it relies on being kept constantly charged in order to provide a discharge ability through its load. It is, therefore, very useful for maintaining a fairly smooth supply voltage in electronics, and this is its prime application—in power supply circuits. It can also be used where large value capacitance and small space are important provisions.

There are shortcomings with this type that the constructor must observe; namely, relatively high leakage current due to the lower resistance to d.c. than in other types, and the shorter life. If a capacitor breaks down, it is more likely to be an electrolytic than any other type. This does not seem to represent a rosy impression of it, but it is widely used for its cheapness, *pro rata* with its capacitance value, compared with others. However, the modern equivalent using an oxide film dielectric has considerably reduced problems common with older types.

Tantalum

Tantalum capacitors are a fairly recent development that compromise size with capacitance and price to obtain a superior product to the conventional electrolytic, with greater life, reliability, and improved tolerance ratings. Although they were expensive a few years ago, they are now competing strongly with the electrolytic for capacitance values up to about 100μF. They are also available in lower values down to about 100 nF.

The tantalum is easily recognised because it looks a little like a small pear shaped bead, often of a deep red colour, although those that do not carry figure and letter markings are given colour code ratings as shown in Fig. 11 F; notice the two different code markings. As in the case of electrolytics the positive plate (or anode) wire is marked with a red or other colour small spot.

Their range of application is almost endless, ranging from decoupling to timing. Whereas a tradional electrolytic capacitor, as described in the previous section, has an aluminium oxide dielectric, the tantalum type uses tantalum oxide, by making the anode a porous block of compressed and sintered powder and coating it with tantalum oxide in an electrolytic bath. It is impregnated with manganese nitrate and heated. The result is an oxide dielectric with a semiconducting coating of manganese dioxide.

The advantages of the tantalum type are not only in their smaller relative size compared with the aluminium oxide electrolytic, but also in the extended temperature range, even in sub-zero environments. One limitation is the maximum working voltage, which makes them particularly suitable for transistor circuits running at low voltage (below about 60 V). The scarcity of raw materials makes them rather higher in price, so it is usual for them to be confined to military and industrial applications.

Paper and Plastics

For many years, the common general-purpose capacitors found in radio and television sets have been paper types. However, these are fast disappearing from the scene because of the adoption of more reliable and smaller capacitors that are easier to manufacture with plastics dielectrics. In both, however, the principle of manufacture involves high speed rolling of foil and dielectric to make a compact unit. One disadvantage of the paper type is its inability to be corrected if, during rolling, there is a 'leakage' path because of some flaw in the paper. Plastics types can be supercharged after rolling to 'burn out' such a defect, resulting in a much lower rejection rate. Consequently, plastics capacitors are relatively cheap to make and can be controlled to closer tolerance limits. Whereas paper types need to be treated by impregnation with wax or liquid plastics, the plastics types do not need this treatment.

Paper capacitors have always had a reputation for reliability in applications using valves and have traditionally been made for voltage ratings (d.c.) of 100 or more volts. Some of the very high voltage types are still made with paper. They are used in stage coupling and decoupling circuits and even where modest amounts of smoothing are required. Although sometimes found in power supply units, they are required to be fairly large to be effective enough, so they are usually replaced by electrolytic types. Tolerances can be quite high in some examples; where needed for controlled tuned circuits, it is best to use a mica or ceramic type.

Plastics

Plastics has played an increasingly important role in the making of capacitors, as implied in the preceding paragraphs. There are different types with differing characteristics, but as a general rule the most popular are the polyester (otherwise technically termed polyethylene terephthalate or Melinex), the polystyrene and polytetrafluorethylene (p.t.f.e.). Many of the applications of paper capacitors have now been taken over by the polyester types and the most obvious advantage is the physical size because the amount of protective covering needed is not as great. Furthermore, they can be made by rolling in the usual way and then formed by squeezing so that the finished unit is flat, making it more amenable to printed circuit board layouts. It is also easier to mark the value by a colour code dipping process. Progress as has been seen is more for the benefit of easier manufacture so keeping costs down, with accompanying improved strength of materials. Insulation resistance is better and temperature range extended.

Polystyrene is a suitable alternative where high stability is required, but they are not expected to tolerate such a wide temperature range. However, because of the improved stability of both polyester and polystyrene types they are more happy in tuned circuits and other critical applications than would be expected of the paper types. Temperature of $70^{\circ}C$ is considered to be the optimum limit for polystyrene types.

The insulation resistance and power factor of all three of these plastics types is very good; however, p.t.f.e. types are not favoured because of the lower dielectric constant and hence the physical size is comparatively larger. In spite of this, p.t.f.e. will withstand very high temperatures. Polycarbonite capacitors have similar properties but have a better power factor and lower temperature rating than polyester types.

Mica

Mica capacitors have been used for several decades and can still hold their own as a reliable, stable, close tolerance, versatile capacitor useful for almost any applications, especially at radio frequencies where high-Q tuned circuits are required. Silvered mica types can be used up to about 100mA current; above this it is better to use foil types. It is not recommended that any one mica capacitor should be expected to handle more than 250 V r.m.s. It is better to connect a group in series for such high voltages. Capacitance ranges are from about 50 to 10 000 pF. The cost of mica types is high and is likely to increase due to shortage of supply of mica in usable sizes and quantities. Because of this, ceramic capacitors offer a competitive alternative, being available in a very versatile range of sizes, shapes and capacitance values. They can be almost 'tailored' with a built-in dielectric constant in either the low-K or high-K range as shown in Table 11. The temperature coefficient can be equally wide ranging, making the ceramic types suitable for almost any environment and application. They are notably famous for use in oscillator and stable tuned circuits; the high-K types can be formed in high capacitance samples for decoupling due to their relatively small size, while the power factor is appreciably higher.

Ceramics are made from one of a number of basic materials, so the the appropriate one can be selected for the required characteristic. It is common to find the titanium dioxide and magnesium titanate types made in tubular form with a colour coded marking for the value. Fig. 11 shows the range of shapes currently available although this is not claimed to be all of them; other shapes are discs rods, cups and plates. It is not usual to find the maximum d.c. working voltage marked on most of them because they will often withstand 500 V each and in many cases even more. However, it is not wise to assume this and if in doubt the constructor should consult the manufacturer's data sheet. Capacitance values range from 1pF up to 100nF. In Table 10 the temperature coefficient coding is deciphered as N = negative, P = positive, and the number indicates the coefficient in parts per million per degree centigrade, for example N470 = 470×10^{-6} = negative temperature coefficient of 470 parts per million per $^{\circ}$C.

Variable Capacitors

Variable capacitors are larger versions of the fixed value types with provision for adjusting the capacitance either by altering the area of overlap of the plates or the distance between them. The dielectrics frequently used are air (for tuning of radio receivers), mica or ceramic for preset controls. The plates are called vanes, there being a fixed set and a moving set, the latter being electrically connected to the frame or chassis, in the air types. They are made in single-gang, twin-gang and triple-gang versions whereby all sets of moving vanes are controlled simultaneously. Fig. 15 shows an enclosed type of variable capacitor which is found in many modern transistor radios.

For reliable long-term results, the vanes should be kept clean and the bearings free running. Preset or trimmer types will often have a

Fig. 15. Variable capacitor

Type found in modern transistor
radios. The dielectric is a plastics
film and the whole capacitor is
enclosed in a plastics box to avoid
damage to the delicate vanes and
to exclude dust

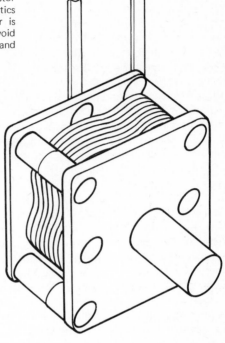

screwdriver slot control and mica or plastics dielectric insulation
leaves which must be reasonably protected from accidental damage.
The two sets of vanes must never be allowed to touch at any point or
there is a risk or circuit failure or damage to other components. It is
equally important when mounting that there is no undue connection
between the frame and any other part of the circuit unless there is a
deliberate requirement for this. If using a twin or three-gang version
with different size or numbers of plates, make quite sure that the
correct set is connected to the appropriate part of the circuit.

It is possible with many air dielectric types to adjust the moving
plate distances by carefully bending the slotted outer vanes slightly
away from the others; they should never be allowed to touch any other
vane or frame. A better way to adjust the capacitance setting is to fit a
trimmer in parallel so that the two connections are directly joined to

45

the rotor and stator connections of the main capacitor. The absolute minimum capacitance setting of the trimmer will rarely, if ever, be zero and manufacturers quote a minimum and maximum capacitance for each sample type.

It is useful to remember when fitting, aligning and calibrating tuning scales that the minimum capacitance setting, i.e. with the vanes fully open, corresponds to the highest frequency on the scale, and therefore it is probably best to close up the vanes as far as possible on both the tuning and trimming capacitors before setting the tuning cursor to the lowest frequency setting on the scale. The trimmer will serve to adjust, or bring in line, the range of frequencies that are required, without having to make physical adjustment to the main control; this has to be be preset when setting up or aligning the equipment and will rarely need any further alteration.

Feed-throughs and Stand-offs

These are very descriptive terms for capacitors of very low value made by using the principle of passing a conductor through or adjacent to the common earth line or chassis (Fig. 14b). They are invariably chassis mounted and consist of a pin set in a glass or ceramic mounting that is fitted to the chassis plate. They are of very low value capacitance, often less than 1pF, being primarily useful for v.h.f. and u.h.f. applications. They should not be confused with chassis mounted tags. The mountings must always be treated with care as any damage could seriously alter its value.

Capacitance Effects

Capacitance effects can be deliberately or accidentally created in or by other components. If they are sufficient to interfere with the correct operation of the circuit, especially at high frequencies, the capacitance will need to be kept as low as possible. Examples are commonly found quoted for cables, inductors and valves.

4 Inductors and transformers

Inductors make use of the electromagnetic principle of electron flow. Therefore, any wire can be considered as an inductor, but for practical purposes is rarely considered in this way because the inductance would be too low to be useful.

If we take a wire and coil it (Fig. 16a), we have concentrated the magnetic properties into a confined space and can design or predict the value of that inductance in henries or fractions of a henry (the unit of inductance). What is inductance? It is a measure of the ability of the

Fig. 16. Inductance

Fig. 16a. Magnetic field set up when current flows through a conductor wound as a coil

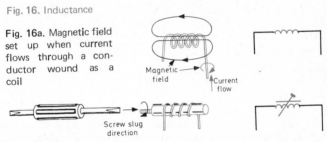

Magnetic field

Current flow

Screw slug direction

Fig. 16b. The magnetic field can be influenced by the insertion of a metallic core. A ferrite or iron core will increase the inductance and a brass core or slug will reduce the inductance

coiled wire to induce a current to flow when passed through a magnetic field, or conversely the coil will produce a magnetic field itself when a current flows through the wire.

In straightforward single coils the magnetic effect can be controlled by placing or adjusting the position of a slug of brass or iron within the coil (Fig. 16b); brass slugs are used in radio and television receivers where the coils are very small and it would be otherwise difficult to reduce the inductance which is also very small. By inserting a brass slug the inductance is decreased; by inserting an iron dust or 'ferrite'

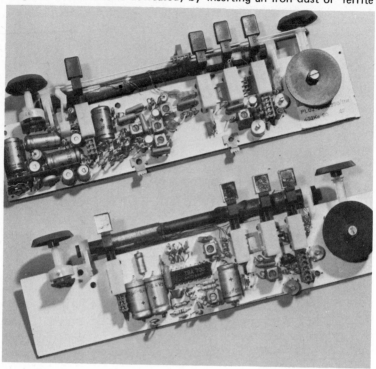

Portable radio receiver with ferrite rod aerial and small i.f. transformers in the centre (top); The integrated circuit equivalent is shown next to it (courtesy NV Philips Gloeilampenfabrieken)

core the inductance is increased. Brass slugs are often preferred where there is also a requirement for robustness, whereas a ferrite slug can be easily broken. Brass slugs are screwdriver adjusted and ferrites screwdriver or hexagonal key adjusted. Fixed value inductors are often wound on an insulating tube or former of plastics or card or some other

Fig. 17. Coils

A typical coil used for radio frequency applications. This one is a wave wound type to minimise the inherent capacitance of the winding. The former is a plastics tube threaded to accommodate an adjustable core

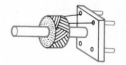

non-magnetic rod; the ends are terminated by soldering to stout wire fixed to the former.

Radio coils for very high frequency have a few turns and the spacing between each turn is often critical and should not be interfered with. At u.h.f. the length of the connecting wires is also very critical since very low inductances are employed to process the signals. Slugs should be adjusted with a non-magnetic (e.g. plastics) trimming tool.

Because of the close proximity of adjacent turns, every coil will have an in-built capacitance, which should be kept to a minimum to avoid upsetting the properties of the tuned circuit as a whole. In medium-wave and long-wave receivers this problem is reduced by using 'wave-wound' coil; these are carefully wound like a ball of string with each layer of wire at a different angle from the previous one (Fig. 17).

Fig. 18. Colour code

Gold indicates decimal point position

Mil. identification

First digit

Second digit

Body colour

Tolerance

Multiplier

	DIGIT	MULTIPLIER
Black	0	1
Brown	1	10
Red	2	100
Orange	3	1,000
Yellow	4	
Green	5	
Blue	6	
Violet	7	
Grey	8	
White	9	

Colour coding used on some very small inductors. These must not be confused with resistors

Coils rarely have any markings on them to identify their inductance because they are often tailored to a specific application (but see Fig. 18). A type number may be given but will mean nothing in itself. One can measure the inductance if required using an inductance bridge

Close-up view of modern miniature i.f. transformers (courtesy General Instrument (UK) Ltd.)

49

measuring instrument. However, this is often outside the scope of many constructors and one has to rely on identification by knowing the type number or making an intelligent guess as to a likely application from the appearance of the component. This rather unsatisfactory state of affairs is largely due to the fact that manufacturers make coils for specific applications and never expect them to be replaced in the set's lifetime.

It is also a fact that tuning coils for radio and television are not specified in terms of inductance to anyone but the designer; it is accepted

Fig. 19. Tuned circuits

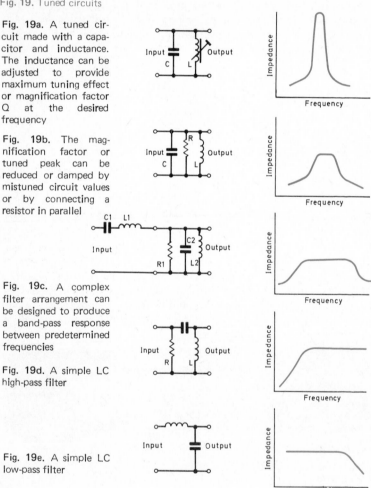

Fig. 19a. A tuned circuit made with a capacitor and inductance. The inductance can be adjusted to provide maximum tuning effect or magnification factor Q at the desired frequency

Fig. 19b. The magnification factor or tuned peak can be reduced or damped by mistuned circuit values or by connecting a resistor in parallel

Fig. 19c. A complex filter arrangement can be designed to produce a band-pass response between predetermined frequencies

Fig. 19d. A simple LC high-pass filter

Fig. 19e. A simple LC low-pass filter

that they are described as, for example 'line scan coil', 'frame oscillator coil', 'medium-wave r.f. coil', or '10.7 MHz i.f. coil'; the actual details complying with standard practice in the application quoted, so that it can often be assumed that the inductance is a standard value. It only remains, therefore, to add the 'standard' capacitance to complete the

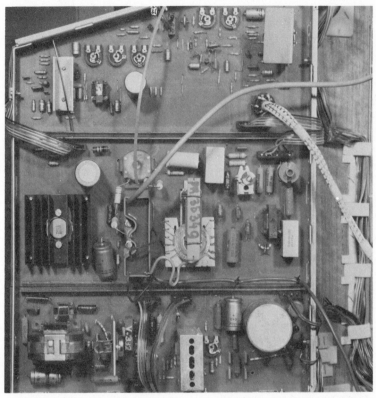

A p.c.b. containing deflection stages for a television receiver. Two ferrite components are obvious here: top left is frame output transformer; centre is the line timebase coil (courtesy NV Philips Gloeilampenfabrieken)

tuned circuit. Special coils designed for a non-standard application will have the inductance quoted so that the constructor can calculate the required capacitance. Fig. 19 shows some uses of inductors in tuned circuits and filters.

There are other details that are rarely quoted but can have an important bearing on the special application; it is often wise to make or

51

wind one's own coils for these purposes in the knowledge of what is required, or by following instructions from a designer. It is quite likely that such features as the Q-factor and frequency range of core is important and one should not deviate in any way from the design specification, especially when using ferrite pot core or rod assemblies. Even points such as spacing between coils and the size of gap in the core can have an important bearing on performance.

Fig. 20. Ferrite pot cores

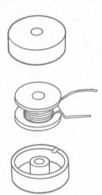

Fig. 20a. A ferrite pot core assembly opened up to show the end plates, core and wound bobbin. A clamp and tag strip would be added

Fig. 20b. Another pot core assembly using symmetrical core halves with a gap made between the two centre core rods

The characteristics of individual ferrite core assemblies vary considerably from type to type, but it can be considered that these have distinctly better properties for highly selective tuned circuits or filters than any other type. They are particularly suitable for high frequency applications up to v.h.f. but would not be worthwhile in very low frequency broadband applications, because their characteristic high-Q response would not be to advantage. Details of characteristics and types are obtainable from the various manufacturers and often they can give guidance on winding information. When ordering, make sure that all relevant parts of the pot core assembly are quoted in their correct number or you may be given only part of it. Examples are shown in Fig. 20.

Iron-cored Inductors

Although this description may seem a little crude, it implies the use of cores (for inductors) made from one of the recognised iron alloys, such as mumetal, stalloy, radiometal. These alloys are treated so that they have special electromagnetic characteristics suitable for audio or r.f. applications. The cores are usually made by interleaving thin plates of the metal which are then inserted into the centre of the coil or bobbin assembly. The plates are called laminations and are available in pairs comprising shapes known as U and T or E and I. For full interleaving the U and T sections are used, providing maximum coupling, but this has the disadvantage of presenting higher core losses. By arranging an air gap in the core, peak flux density is reduced and winding resistance increased, thus reducing core loss. The effective Q factor can be adjusted by alteration of the air gap. Fig. 21 shows laminated cores.

In laminated cores, it is important to ensure effective insulation between each lamination to minimise core eddy currents; when assembling the core this insulation must be arranged on the same relative side of each lamination piece. The bobbin should be filled tight with the laminations to prevent vibration or wedged by inserting a thinner section as the last piece. Clamps must effectively grip and squeeze the laminations together without risk of damage to them or the insulation; any slightly damaged laminations should always be discarded to prevent later problems after final assembly and wiring.

In spite of the precautions and care often taken in this assembly, there is sometimes a risk of vibration occurring in the laminations and even in the winding itself, especially at low frequencies, giving rise to an irritating buzz. If this is experienced it is usually a sign that there is some slackness and, on new assemblies, can often be overcome by impregnation. Manufacturers adopt various methods of doing this. In most cases the result is satisfactory. Among these the most reliable is by vacuum impregnated beeswax, the process being best done over a period of about two hours' immersion in a hot wax bath. This is a time consuming process, so it is sometimes replaced by varnish impregnation. If the constructor experiences further vibration problems, the best course of action is to allow molten beeswax to drip onto the windings and the laminations, especially around exposed edges and joins. To avoid being wasteful, the beeswax can be melted by a hot soldering iron held over the appropriate parts of the assembly. There may be a temptation to use paraffin wax from a candle, which would do the same job, but this is not recommended, particularly for power or mains transformers and inductors, because of the inherent risks from the water content in such wax.

Fig. 21. Iron cores

Fig. **21a.** A laminated core type of inductance. The coil is wound on a bobbin in the centre and the laminations clamped to prevent vibration

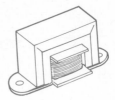

Fig. **21b.** Laminated cores used for transformers and choke inductors

Fig. **21c.** T and U section laminations are alternately interleaved

Fig. **21d.** E and I section laminations arranged to provide a deliberate gap in the core to minimise eddy current effects

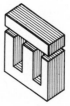

Fig. **21e.** A single pair of C-core section laminations

Fig. **21f.** A triple-C core used where space limitations are prevalent

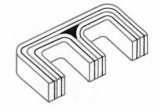

Transformers

What has been said about inductors applies also to transformers, which are only extensions of the electromagnetic principles employed. When a coil of wire is energised, a magnetic field is created. By changing the strength or polarity of this field in the close proximity of another coil, a secondary current will flow in sympathy in this secondary coil, by means of induction. A constant d.c. current through one winding will have no effect in the secondary. The relationship between the two windings mounted on the common core can be determined. In a perfect example, this relationship is that the ratio of voltage at any instant is equal to the ratio of the number of turns of wire for each winding; conversely, this ratio is inversely proportional to the current flowing in each winding. Fig. 22 shows how a transformer may be used to make a tuned circuit.

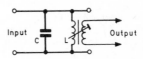

Fig. 22. A tuned circuit

using a capacitor and transformer

If we could make a perfect transformer, there would be no problems, but unfortunately, as we implied in the earlier paragraphs, there are core losses through eddy currents being established in the core

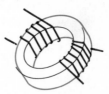

Fig. 23. A ring core or toroid

usually made from ferrite materials and coated with a vitreous insulation

material, since the core is resistive and capable of carrying an induced current. The degree of induction depends to a large extent on the nature and construction of the core used, and its response at the frequency of operation. In the case of ferrite materials with an air gap in the core (Fig. 23) the eddy current can be made negligible, but where an inductor or transformer operates close to or above saturation point, i.e. when the core is fully magnetised, this current is detrimental to the applied circuit and can be damaging, with a risk of overheating, to the assembly.

The windings must be designed to be capable of carrying the expected maximum load current and will be thicker for the heavier current required. It is always worth using an over-rated winding because, with thicker wire, the resistance will be lower and hence winding losses minimised. Of course, there is an optimum winding specification which has to allow for these factors in conjunction with the size and cost of the transformer. Where there is a lack of experience or training in transformer design, it is often best to buy ready made samples rated according to your needs. However, it is worth knowing something about the points described here so that the purchase is an intelligent one and not likely to lead to disastrous results.

When you have purchased your transformer, how will you know if it is suitable or even correctly made? It is fairly easy in the case of mains types to feed into the primary the mains supply and measure the voltage on the secondary winding, although this may be higher than you might expect because the designer should have allowed for a small drop when the winding is connected to its load. It is almost impossible to tell if the wire gauge used for the winding is adequate without stripping the transformer, but by comparison with a known sample or by experience, one can often hazard an intelligent assessment by looking at the wire emerging from the winding to the tag connections, assuming that an intermediate connecting lead has not been used. Standard copper wire tables usually give the maximum recommended current for the gauge of wire.

If the winding is connected to a load resistance (this can be made up from light bulbs for mains transformers) the voltage measured across this load should be correct for the quoted winding current. Any *serious* change in voltage will probably result in overheating of the core and/or winding and the load will be too high for safe operation. Of course, the load must be adequately rated to allow the required current flow without overheating. Often a transformer that is inadequate will be generally too small and, by comparison with known commercial examples of repute, one can assess whether the sample is likely to be big enough for the job.

In the case of audio frequency or r.f. transformers, whether wound on laminated, ferrite or air cored formers, one cannot make these tests. The experience and comparison with reputable types will usually help, but there are a few basic points worth remembering. Again the physical size can be an important factor where a good low frequency response is required; the smaller the transformer, the worse will be this l.f. response. One can also be reasonably sure that a small transformer uses thin wire, giving a higher resistance or source impedance than would be accepted for efficient matching to the circuit. The winding resistance should be kept to a minimum, commensurate with the frequency range being handled. Core size should be as large as practicable to reduce core losses and improve efficiency.

56

R.F. coils and transformers having air cores or brass slugs can be made very small and with very thin wire because the response within the audio frequency range is insignificant to the application. However, other factors become important, such as inter-winding capacitance and close coupling, this being minimised by using very thin wire. Winding capacitance can have a detrimental effect on the response within the tuned frequency range and can be considerably reduced, as in mains transformers, by inserting an inter-winding screen which is connected to 'earth' potential. However, this would increase the self-capacitance of the winding, which must be taken into account in the application. To reduce additionally induced current in the screen, this should be kept short and not joined in a continuous loop.

Magnetic interaction between two components or between one electromagnetic component and adjacent wiring, can be reduced by using electrostatic screening. This would comprise the insertion of a metallic shield between them which is connected to 'earth' potential. In the case of mains and audio equipment it would be a magnetic material such as mumetal; for higher frequencies, above 1kHz and particularly in high-impedance circuits, a non-magnetic material such as copper or aluminium would be used. A typical example is the braided shield in coaxial and screened cables.

Tapped Windings

Transformers are frequently found to use tapped windings, that is connection is made to one or more points along the length of wire in the windings (Fig. 24). Where a centre tap is quoted then the tapped take-off point is half-way along the winding and should result in two equal voltage outputs joined together in series. If the winding is long, there might be an undesirable mismatch between these two halves which, as in the case of audio amplifiers, would give a mismatch between the two half-cycles of the waveform processed. To reduce this problem, the two halves can be wound simultaneously to ensure that both are exactly the same length; there would be no problems arising from the minimum and maximum winding diameters as in the conventional approach. This form of winding is called 'bifilar' winding.

Centre-tapped windings are often used in power rectifying circuits, and in 'balanced' audio circuits where positive and negative half-cycles are processed separately. Other tapped windings might provide a selection of voltages or different impedance outputs.

Where a transformer is used in an oscillator circuit, it is usually important to observe the relationship between the winding terminations to keep the correct phase relationship. This is also an important feature in the connection of inductive loads, such as loudspeakers, to phase related outputs, such as in stereo and quadraphonic sound equipment.

Fig. 24. Mains transformer

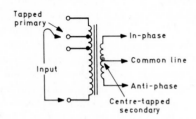

An example of a mains trans-former with voltage selection tappings on the primary winding and a centre tapped secondary for bridge rectifier circuits

For this purpose, one of the two terminals is indicated in some way to aid identification of phase (Fig. 25). It might be a coloured spot or a + sign or a black dot on the circuit symbol. In these applications the polarity must be observed in order to achieve the correct results. Where

Fig. 25. Audio transformer

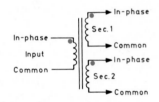

A phased winding signal trans-former often found in audio circuits, as push-pull drivers. The spot denotes the relative phase polarity

phase relationship is important but no such identification is evident, then the constructor must determine by experiment which is the correct way of connecting; it is unlikely that damage will result in a.c. circuits through incorrect phase connection.

5 Semiconductor devices

Semiconductor devices include diodes, thyristors, triacs, transistors and integrated circuits; however, this chapter will discuss all of these except integrated circuits, which can be found in the next chapter. All semiconductors described here rely on the behaviour of doped materials formed on silicon or germanium substrates. To the layman, they will apply to devices that can replace the functions of thermionic valves by providing a means to process a signal, but by using low voltage d.c. supplies or no other activating supply at all.

Diodes

Diodes operating without any influence other than the applied a.c. signal will act as rectifiers, that is, they will pass only that portion of the signal which is either positive or negative with respect to a zero datum reference, according to the way that the diode is connected. They have only two terminals, which may be brought out as wires or tags; some even use the component body for one connection.

Small-signal diodes are usually capable of passing up to 250 mA at about 50 V. They should not be confused with resistors from their appearance even though there may be some resemblence. Apart from an identifying type number marked on the body, one should look for a spot or band around one end to identify the cathode connection; this may be marked with a plus (+) sign. These components are frequently used to act as detectors in radio receivers, limiters in pulse circuits, or gating diodes in logic circuits.

Small diodes are suitable for mounting direct onto printed circuit boards without any means of conducting surplus heat away, since they rarely need to be subjected to high currents, especially as larger types are available for this purpose. However, one must treat them with caution when soldering as excess heat can permanently damage the device. (Later we shall discuss the general rules to adopt in handling semiconductor devices.)

Fig. 26. Diodes

The diode symbol and a selection of case outlines

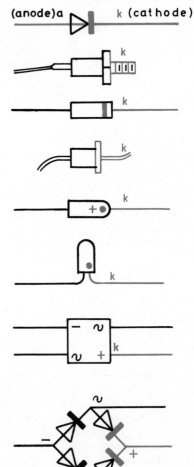

Fig. 27. Rectifiers

The bridge rectifier outline and symbol

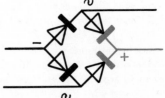

Larger diodes used for rectification in power-supply circuits are designed to handle relatively high current and consequently will generate some heat which needs to be shunted away from the device to prevent heat build-up and damage. These are often found in strong metallic body encapsulations which are sometimes made with a screw thread for bolting to the chassis or heat sink plate. It is important, therefore, not to allow this body or heat sink to come into contact with any other component or wiring than that intended for it. Identification of the polarity of these types may vary from sample to sample; some examples are given in Fig. 25. Several diodes may be connected in a bridge circuit in a single encapsulation for power-supply circuits, as shown in Fig. 27.

Zener diodes may, at first glance, look like some ordinary diodes, since they are often about the same size and shape as the small signal types. Only identification of the type number will help. In any case where the type number has been erased, one has no evidence as to what it is and it is not wise to make assumptions. The voltage rating of a zener diode indicates that the device will generally not exceed that voltage across its terminals when supplied from a higher one. This is because the zener diode acts as a kind of voltage dropper as well as a rectifier. However, there are limits as to how much work they can be expected to do without total breakdown and this is determined by the power rating of the device.

Fig. 28. Zener diodes

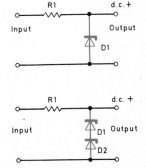

Fig. 28a. Zener diode connected as a voltage stabiliser on a d.c. line

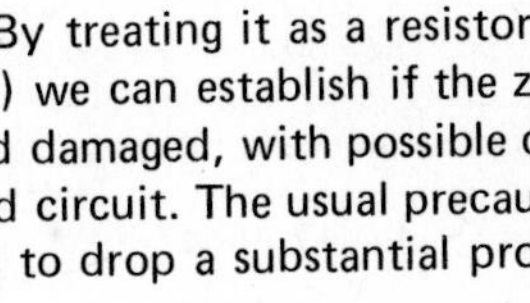

Fig. 28b. Two zener diodes can be connected in series to handle a higher voltage

Using Ohm's law, one can easily assess the current handling ability of the device, just as we do with resistors. By treating it as a resistor in a potential divider network (see Chapter 2) we can establish if the zener diode is likely to become overheated and damaged, with possible damage to other components in its associated circuit. The usual precaution is to connect a series resistor, calculated to drop a substantial proportion of the required reduction (Fig. 28).

The zener is best used in conditions which are reasonably within its power rating capabilities, but will offer some degree of regulation of a supply voltage in the presence of modest fluctuations, caused for example by surges from pulses on the supply line. It may also be used to great advantage with a d.c. transistor amplifier in power supply stabilisers, where a low voltage fluctuation is translated into a current compensation circuit. They can be used as trigger control diodes in thyristor applications. One of the features of the zener diode is that one can use two in series to operate at a combined voltage, but parallel connection is not advised because of power sharing problems.

Tunnel diodes are not often used but come into their own as high-speed switches at high frequencies. They operate on the principle of reducing current with increasing voltage applied after reaching a certain point of negative resistance. They can also operate as a high-frequency amplifier or oscillator in terms of megahertz. These diodes look very much like small versions of the 'top-hat' encapsulation, the cathode being at the broadest end.

Fig. 29. Thyristors

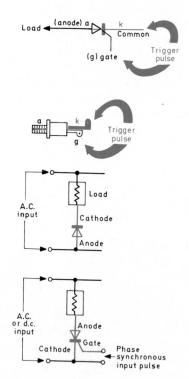

Fig. 29a. The thyristor or silicon controlled rectifier symbol and an example of a common case outline. More outlines are shown in a later diagram

Fig. 29b. A very simple way of providing unidirectional flow of current through the load

Fig. 29c. The current through the load can be switched on and off by application of a pulse to the gating input of a thyristor, which acts as a switched diode

62

Other diode devices can be classified in the group known as thyristors (Fig. 29), which are effectively switched diodes, being triggered into a conducting state by a separate pulse applied to the gate terminal.

Thyristors and Triacs

Thyristors are sometimes called silicon controlled rectifiers (s.c.r.) which is probably the best descriptive name ever given to a semiconductor device. The principle is that the main a.c. current (or it can be d.c.) is rectified by the normal diode action (Fig. 29b) but will only conduct when the applied trigger voltage at the gate terminal exceeds a certain amount (Fig. 29c). It ceases to conduct when either that voltage is reduced below the given threshold or the gate current is switched off altogether.

Thyristors are often used in switching the a.c. mains supply and by devious means to limit the VA (volt-amps) product available to the load at predetermined instances. In the former case the technique used is called burst-firing, in which the switching takes place when the supply voltage crosses the zero voltage datum. In the latter, voltage is switched at a point where both the voltage and current reach the same proportion of the peak figure. This is called phased switching; it has the serious disadvantage of creating a chopped waveform which, if applied to the mains supply will give rise to interference effects to nearby a.m. radio. In this case, suitable suppression filters have to be connected to the switching circuit. The major advantage is in the ability of this switching circuit to reduce the voltage applied to the load without serious loss of power; hence its application to lamp dimming. The trigger pulses are derived from a small proportion of the supply and kept in phase with the load current.

To achieve better switching of a.c. supplies, there is an advantage in using a triac (Fig. 30), which performs the same kind of function but switches on both positive- and negative-going half-cycles of the supply, A smoother output with reduced interference will be achieved, while switching can be arranged to occur on both positive and negative pulses or a choice of one or the other.

Both unidirectional and bidirectional switching thyristors and triacs must use one of the main terminals as a common line for both gating and main load currents. Their connections are shown in Fig. 31. Encapsulation outlines for both are on similar lines or may even resemble transistors in some cases. It is important to identify the device type and its proper connections before inserting it into the circuit. Notice the different terms used in the terminal annotations. Where these devices are required to operate in conjunction with small-signal transistor circuits other than power-control dimmers or in mains wiring, it may be important for safety and protection of other components, to isolate

Fig. 30. Triacs

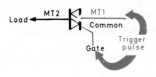

Fig. 30a. The triac symbol

Fig. 30b. Switched a.c. can be supplied to the load by using a triac, the full cycle being used

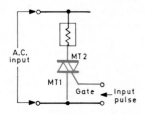

the mains supply completely from the control circuit; in this case one should do so by linking the gating electrodes to the control circuit via an isolating transformer. Since high-speed pulses will be employed, this

Fig. 31. Thyristors and triacs

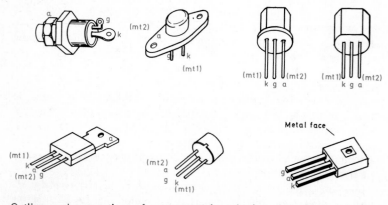

Outlines and connections of a representative selection of thyristors and triacs

transformer must be capable of handling them. It is usual to wind a simple 1:1 transformer of about ten to fifteen turns of 36 s.w.g. enamelled copper wire for each winding on a ferrite core, preferably a ring core or toroid made from compressed ferrite material, as in Fig. 32.

The points described later regarding heat sinks apply equally to these devices as much as any other. However, if the constructor obtains devices that are outside the manufacturer's accepted specification, they may be capable of operating, but at the risk of excessive heat dissipation or high gating currents, in which case allowance must be made for this in designing the circuit and heat sink. These devices will most likely not have a genuine type number identification that applies. In mains supply applications it is a wise precaution to ensure top-grade samples are used to avoid any risks from unknown or faulty operation.

Fig. 32. Pulse transformer

A pulse transformer comprising a small number of turns on a toroid, or ferrite pot core

However, the cause of circuit failure may not necessarily lie in the sample used but in the nature of the trigger pulse applied to it. If a trigger pulse is present at the right time, but not of sufficient amplitude, the device may fail to fire; if the trigger pulse does not decrease sufficiently at the right time, then the device may 'hang up', although this latter symptom can also be caused by saturation.

Transistors

A very wide range of semiconductor devices comes under the umbrella heading of 'transistor', but in most cases it will be recognised as a three-terminal device except in some special types of field-effect transistor. By reference to the companion book to this one, the constructor will find many different types. Unfortunately, one cannot recognise these different classes just by reference to the type number unless one is already familiar with them.

The most common are the bipolar ranges, found in a wide range of domestic electronic entertainment equipment. These have three wire, pin or tag terminals for the collector, base and emitter (Figs. 33, 34, 35), although in some power transistors the collector may be connected directly to the metal case. These are usually intended to be mounted on heat sinks, using the special kit of insulating components that should be supplied with them. Because of the tremendous variation in characteristics and operating conditions, transistors are generally much more versatile than almost any other component, but this does not mean that they can or should be treated with disrespect, because they are, on the other hand, probably the most delicate and liable to destruction of the active parts. The base electrode carries a very small

Fig. 33. Circuit symbols

Circuit symbols of an npn transistor (left), a pnp type (centre) and a field-effect transistor or f.e.t. (right)

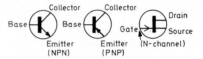

current in order to encourage a larger current flow through the collector. If this were exceeded there would be a risk of permanent damage to the device. In field-effect transistors the risks are very much greater because of the very high impedance of the input gate electrode.

Fig. 34. Transistor encapsulations

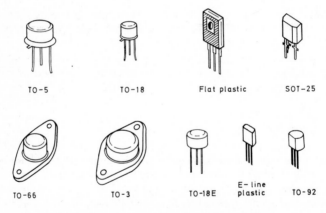

A selection of common transistor encapsulations

Consequently, precautions are taken by manufacturers to help protect them from damage. It is possible to create such excess current flow just from the static charge in a person's body, so that if the constructor touches the gate terminal when it is either unprotected or disconnected from its circuit, damage could result. Soldering irons also have a habit of holding a charge, however small, which can be released from the bit

66

when it touches the terminal; soldered connections should be made to field-effect transistors with the iron temporarily isolated completely from the mains. There is some degree of risk with ordinary bipolar types in this respect and it is a good plan, when soldering small-signal transistors, to take the mains plug out or run your iron from a low voltage isolated a.c. or d.c. supply.

There are numerous handbooks, wall charts, data sheets and text-books that will give details of transistor characteristics; these are published from time to time by the manufacturers and by magazine publishers. Probably the most useful information to acquire will be the maximum rated collector voltage (V_{CEO}), the maximum rated collector current (I_{CEO}) and the current gain expressed as h_{FE} h_{fe} or β. This latter feature may have a wide 'spread' of gain which means that the device has been measured as falling somewhat within that range of current gain. Such a spread is sometimes subdivided into suffixed type numbers or numbered in close numerical sequence, such as in the case of the 'nominal' BC108 which is subdivided and grouped as BC107, BC108, BC109. These are further subdivided for industrial applications where more specific tolerance of gain spread is required.

Transistors are often classified in this sort of way to distinguish between the operating temperature range, such as 0 to 70°C for consumer applications, and the more expensive wider range types for military and industrial applications, especially for use in tropical climates.

Unmarked or unfamiliar code numbers tell the constructor nothing except that the device is most likely outside the accepted specification in the manufacturer's data sheets or that the device has been recoded by another firm who might have put a batch through a series of measuring procedures and recoded the device according to their find-ings. In these cases there is no guarantee of quality other than that offered by the supplier; constructors are well advised to ascertain the origins of devices that do not carry the manufacturer's official trade mark, and from this find out the performance specification.

A large proportion of the transistors available can be mounted by soldering direct to a printed circuit board type of layout. It is most important to be sure about the connections because if a mistake is made and the power switched on, not only could the device be damaged, but a chain reaction can be set up, so causing damage to several other components in the circuit. Insulation of power transistors, mounted on a heat sink, is achieved best by using the correct insulating mica washer, nylon fixing screws and silicon grease; never overtighten any transistor fixing screw or leave the mounting so loose that acciden-tal movement of the device can lead to a short circuit.

Fig. 35. Transistor identification

CONNECTION SPACING (mm approx.)

e to c	2 mm	TO1

e to b	11 mm	
fixing holes	30 mm apart, 4BA	
line eb to c	13·5 mm	TO3

e to b	5 mm	TO5

e to c	6 mm	TO7
(case wire approx. in centre)		

e to c	7·5 mm	TO8

e to c	3·8 mm	TO18

e to b	5 mm	TO66
fixing holes	24 mm apart	
line eb to c	8·7 mm	

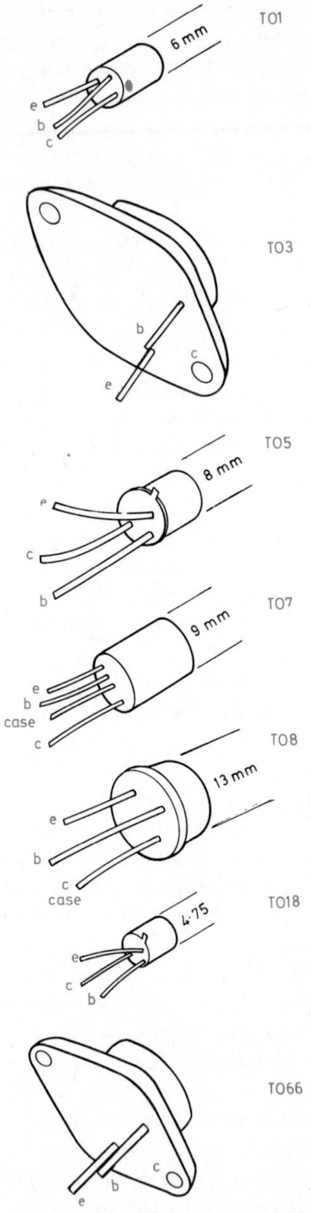

Leadout arrangements and identification of some of the most common transistors. Reference should be made to manufacturer's data for specific types

68

Fig. 35. (contd).
CONNECTION SPACING (mm approx.)

c to dia. opp.	2·5 mm
outer leads	3 mm
e to b	2·5 mm
c to opp	3 mm
e to c	5 mm
e to c	2·5 mm
e to b	3 mm
e to c	3 mm
e to c	2·5 mm
e to b	5 mm

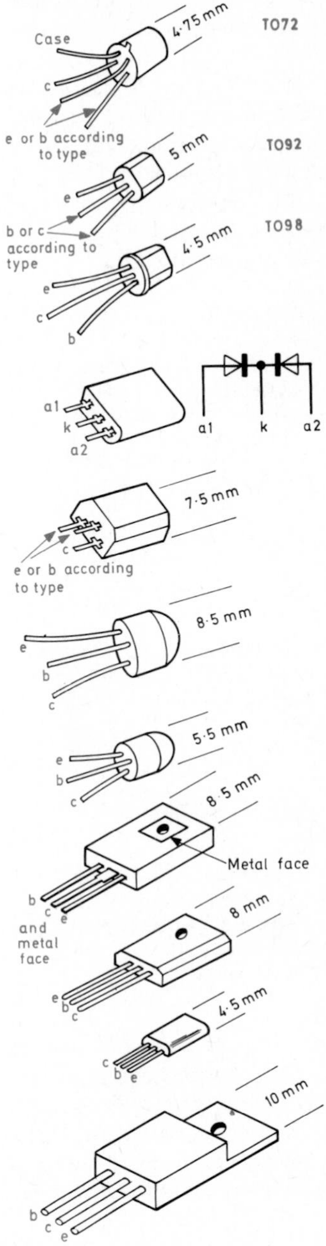

Case

4·75 mm   TO72

c

e or b according
to type

5 mm   TO92

e

b or c
according to
type

4·5 mm   TO98

e

c

b

a1
k
a2

a1   k   a2

7·5 mm

c

e or b according
to type

8·5 mm

e

b

c

5·5 mm

e

b

c

8·5 mm

Metal face

b
c
e
and
metal
face

8 mm

e b
c

4·5 mm

c b e

10 mm

b
c
e

69

When wire terminated types are fitted, make sure after soldering that the wires do not touch each other or any other metal object except the intended connection point. They are best handled with a pair of long-nosed wiring pliers, which will also act as a heat shunt while soldering (Fig. 36); never bend the wires any nearer the point of entry into the encapsulation than 3 mm to avoid risks of fracture to the encapsulation (Fig. 37a). If it is necessary to cross wires to match printed circuit layouts use insulating sleeving of about 0.5 mm diameter (Fig. 37b). Never assume that the leadout arrangement automatically matches the printed circuit layout, especially where a substitute transistor is being fitted.

Fig. 36. Heat shunt

When mounting and soldering any wire-ended semiconductor device, hold the wire being soldered with a pair of long-nosed pliers to shunt away some of the heat from the device

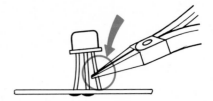

Fig. 37.

Fig. 37a. Never bend the wire leads of transistors closer than about 3 mm from the encapsulation

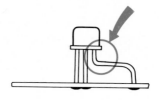

Fig. 37b. Centre leads that have to be bent across the path of other leads should be insulated. If they are allowed to touch when in use the device could be damaged

Transistors are unique in one respect: they are not made as direct replacements between one type and another, such as could be arranged with thermionic valves. There is often the misunderstanding that one can find a direct replacement. If the constructor is sufficiently diligent in his researches he could in some cases find replacements, but the general policy now, especially under recent trading laws, is to deny the fact to avoid making any likely statements of intent or fitness for specific applications. Because of the wide range of specifications, it is an impossible task to classify all types of direct equivalents and the tendency in published lists is to suggest possible alternatives. It should never be assumed that any suggested replacement will be correct both ways, because a suggested replacement is most likely to have a specification of higher rated characteristics than the original type sample. If in any doubt, always consult manufacturers' data sheets.

Unfortunately, a very frustrating situation arose a few years ago, and is still in evidence now, in which equipment made overseas and imported by British manufacturing agents contained some devices that might not be readily recognised. This is particularly the case with transistors and diodes which carry type numbers of the country of origin but are not universally used in this country. Identification is almost impossible unless one can obtain the correct replacement components from the importers. When buying foreign-made equipment, it is always best to ascertain the spares situation before purchase. If a transistor fails, one cannot find out what its characteristics are by measuring.

Heat Sinks

Semiconductor devices that carry appreciable current, often those in excess of about 100mA, will most likely require a heat sink of some kind, although some might have sufficient metal in the encapsulation for modest current levels. A circuit design should specify any heat-sink requirements in addition to this. In many experimental low-current applications a temporary heat sink can be fabricated from a piece of sheet aluminium or copper and then painted matt black. The size or surface area is important if it is to perform its function properly, that is to prevent thermal runaway in the device under normal operating conditions.

Recommendations are given by manufacturers of the device concerned based on an ambient temperature of about 25°C. Neat and attractive heatsinks can be purchased ready made and drilled to suit, within reasonable limits, the style of device case in use (Fig. 38). It is always the total surface area that matters, so in the case of finned heatsinks the amount of surface area is considerably greater for equivalent space occupied by the heatsink. If the mounting holes have to be drilled by the constructor, make sure that all rough edges and burrs are completely removed by filing before attempting to fit the device. The accommodation area should not be overloaded by

Fig. 38. Heat sinks

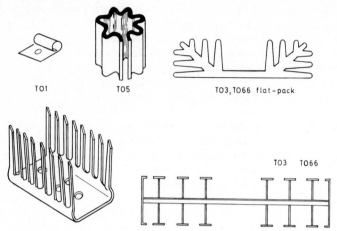

TO1   TO5   TO3, TO66 flat-pack

TO3   TO66

A selection of heat sinks made commercially for power transistors

Vertical deflection circuit board. Notice the heat sink used for the power output transistor has several fins to increase the surface area (courtesy NV Philips Gloeilampenfabrieken)

72

trying to cram in the maximum number of devices because performance will suffer to the ultimate detriment of the devices themselves and probably to other associated components.

In spite of any suggestion that heat-sink compound can totally replace the mica insulating washer, there is just a chance that leakage can occur though a pin-hole at some later date and the constructor should use the mica washer as well. Fixing can be made by using nylon screws or bushes designed specially for the purpose; where the collector is connected to the metal case, a soldering tag connection will be required. Heat sinks should be mounted in free air (large types should not be enclosed) so that the majority of fins are vertical to allow warm air to flow away easily.

6 Integrated circuits

It is probably in connection with computer systems that integrated circuits are best known, but it is possible to find them used in almost any electronic application that uses or processes small signals, both a.c. and d.c. Since there are books that describe the theory and manufacture of i.c.s in great detail, we are best concerned here with the practical side of using them.

First, let us classify them according to their applications and we find that there is a natural grouping into digital or switching circuits and analogue or linear circuits. These are further grouped, for example, in digital circuits there are specific logic systems called TTL (transistor-transistor-logic), DTL (diode-transistor-logic), ECL (emitter-coupled-logic) and the now little used RTL (resistor-transistor-logic). There are other more sophisticated systems using MOS (metal-oxide-silicon) ✱ which are subdivided into further groupings according to their structure. These names do not tell the constructor any more than how the circuitry is based and given an identity. Linear i.c.s are very different and often seem to present a plethora of mixed types apparently made to the individual needs of manufacturers and users. This may be true to some extent, but one can classify many of them in the following broad groups: operational amplifiers, voltage regulators, audio amplifiers, television modules, radio tuners and i.f. amplifiers. There are others, of course.

By studying the range of i.c.s now being made, it is not difficult to imagine that the statement in the opening paragraph implies the tremendous developments in electronics engineering technology over recent years. In spite of controversy as to the future prospects of discrete components, there is little evidence of any decline in the demand for these and one must accept that i.c. technology has helped

74

✱ CMOS. Complementary metal oxide
Semi-conductor (that see MOS
above)

to improve the opportunities of simplified construction, using ready made printed circuit boards and various alternative types of assembly system. Discrete components are still required to be used in conjuction with any integrated circuit in order to convert a fairly standard package into a specific circuit application. The cost of manufacturing a small quantity of original design i.c.s is very high, so the manufacturer aims to produce a series of i.c.s that can be used in a wide variety of finished equipment. They are then made versatile and can be tailored by the constructor. Before he can successfully do this he should have an appreciation of what characteristics to expect and how best to apply them.

Unfortunately, to present all the necessary information on all of the various groups of i.c.s would require devoting a large volume to describing them. However, one can make a limited number of general observations that will hopefully encourage the constructor to delve further as the need arises.

Logic I.C.s

The most popular class of logic circuits have been TTL, since they offer a versatile system of interfacing between different circuits, including DTL, while providing economic switching systems for computation or logic decoding at high speed. The main differences between these groups is in the individual circuit components; it is not necessary to have an intimate knowledge of each of these. Just as long as we know that we can link the i.c.s together, we can trust them as black boxes, selecting an i.c. for its function rather than its intricate detail. In order to design systems in this way, the constructor will need to know what sort of signal can be obtained at each output for a given input. This is easy because the manufacturer will invariably identify the i.c.s with a function description as well as a type number. This may sound easy but unless a few basic rules are followed problems can arise and the user will need to know why and how to rectify them.

In all logic i.c.s the switching operation, inversion or decoding will depend on the clear separation of logic levels, i.e. on or off, '1' or '0', without interference or sporadic triggering from extraneous pulses. In TTL these are usually in the region of 0.4 V and in DTL about 0.7 V, for the 'off' or zero state and equivalent to the positive supply line voltage for the on or '1' state. The exception is in ECL, which uses comparators and has plus and minus voltages for logic levels. The logic notation or truth table is based on this common feature. However, if a stray pulse arrives at the input, maybe via the supply line if inadequately de-coupled, then the circuit may change state. The ability of the i.c. to reject or ignore the effect of unwanted pulses is called the 'noise immunity' and such pulses must be kept below the threshold figure given in the data at all times.

The i.c. has an inbuilt characteristic called the 'propagation delay' time which will suggest a maximum time in which any pulses are likely to cause a change of state. This is determined by the speed of operation of the circuit; the time given for TTL is generally less than for DTL, which means that it will be more prone to spontaneous triggering, so it is necessary to keep power supply lines shorter for TTL—in the region of 12 in (30 cm) maximum. In the case of ECL the switching time, and hence the propagation delay time, will be more critical.

The usual figures to expect are, for TTL, 13 ns for standard versions and as little as 3 ns for high-speed Schottky versions; there is a low power version suffixed L with a delay time of 33 ns. DTL times will be about 25 ns, while for ECL it is about 2.5 ns. Noise immunity figures are, for, TTL, 0.3 V to 1 V; for DTL 0.75 V; for ECL 0.2 V. More precise figures for individual types will be found in manufacturers' data sheets.

Noise immunity and propagation delay times are the most critical of logic i.c. characteristics and often overlooked; constructors then some-times wonder why spurious triggering occurs. Other points worth noting are the current required by one i.c. to operate from a pulse or logic state from the preceding one. This is called the 'sinking current' and determines, in complex systems, how many normal i.c. functions in the same family can be connected to an output. This is called 'fan-out', the number given stating how many normal additional stages can be connected in parallel to the output. In the case of drivers or open-ended output circuits for connection directly to an external load, this figure will be lower; it is often possible to connect a lamp indicator or even a small current relay. The sinking current will determine what sort of load can be applied.

Input devices can be either another i.c. in the same family or some form of triggering device, such as a Schmitt trigger driven from a thresh-old or linear voltage detector circuit, such as a temperature detector bridge or even a low-frequency sine wave. To minimise risks of spon-taneous or spurious triggering it is essential to mount logic i.c. systems on a printed circuit board layout. To this end there are a number of ready-made boards designed to provide the supply lines in a controlled manner and, in some cases, to arrange 'ground planes' (large areas of copper connected to the common line) in such a way that interaction between one part of the circuit and another is prevented by the inter-posed copper. Usually, these boards are designed for use with i.c.s in 'dual-in-line' DIL i.c. packages, copper pads being arranged in rows for the connection of other components and wiring.

Generally, constructors will build their circuits based on one of these systems; it is unlikely that MOS will be used in other than complex systems, since they lend themselves more to direct application in large scale shift registers and memories. They are based on the extension of field-effect transistor technology and present problems in experimental or prototype applications in small-scale systems. They require much higher operating voltages and are limited to operating at pulse repetition frequencies of about 1 MHz. They also have a high input impedance, which demands extra care in handling and soldering by the constructor (see Chapter 5).

Linear I.C.s

Included in this category are operational amplifiers, which is the only group of linear i.c.s that one can use in a wide variety of circuits. The operational amplifier can be wired to form the heart of an analogue computer which translates a voltage reference into a measurable numerical value. It can also be used to compare two voltages and process the difference voltage. By suitable use of feedback components the waveform can be modified, forming an inverter, differentiator or integrator.

Operational amplifiers require both positive and negative voltage supplies to provide an open-loop gain of more than 60dB. Input impedance is high (more than 300 kΩ in many cases and sometimes several megohms); output impedance is low, so that heavy feedback can be applied. The input offset voltage will determine the maximum input signal voltage that can be applied, while the output is usually taken from an emitter follower stage. The differential comparator has a similar input arrangement via two common coupled emitter stages.

Other amplifiers include the wideband types, which are based on the cascading of several differential pairs. They are usually designed for applications up to frequencies of several MHz with medium impedance input and very low impedance output. Positive and negative supply lines are required.

Among those amplifiers now being used for domestic electronic equipment are i.c.s designed for low and high signal levels and some more recent types incorporating the functions of audio stages and i.f. stages on the same silicon slice. Specific features of these can be obtained from individual data sheets. There are no specific rules adopted for them such as are found in logic i.c.s because of the variety of types made. However, there are common factors in the use and mounting of all i.c.s.

Packages

Integrated circuits are made in a number of standard packages as shown in Fig. 39. The most common is the dual-in-line package with eight, fourteen or sixteen pins, although some of the more complex types may have twenty or twentyfour pins, arranged along either side. Numbering is in a clockwise sequence looking at the underside, starting at the end with the notch or semicircular key mark. Where it is difficult to accommodate the connections to adjacent pins, particularly with some linear i.c.s, a 'quad-in-line' package can be used; these are suffixed Q and the pins are pre-formed in a staggered arrangement as shown in Fig. 39e. It will be noticed that the pins of DIL packages are

Fig. 39. Integrated circuits

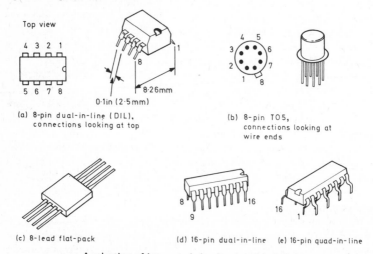

(a) 8-pin dual-in-line (DIL), connections looking at top

(b) 8-pin TO5, connections looking at wire ends

(c) 8-lead flat-pack

(d) 16-pin dual-in-line

(e) 16-pin quad-in-line

A selection of integrated circuit encapsulations

shaped with a shoulder so that when inserted into a printed circuit board there is a very small clearance under the package; this maintains an air passage to prevent heat being directly transferred through the board when soldering and should not be altered.

Having mounted the i.c., do not solder the pin connections until you are absolutely certain that you have the correct i.c. and mounted the right way according to the keyway reference. Mistakes are expensive and difficult to correct once all the pins are soldered. It is possible to remove an i.c. from its mounting after soldering, but will be difficult unless using one of the specially made desoldering tools for the job. Prolonged heat applied to the copper of a p.c.b. can melt it; always use a small iron, 15 W or less, for soldering into place. The use of i.c. holders is recommended to avoid later trouble, except in v.h.f.

Typical packages used for integrated circuits. Top, MOS analogue multiplexers (courtesy SGS-Ates) in TO-5 packages. Also an operational amplifier (courtesy Bourns Trimpot Ltd). Bottom, dual timer circuits in DIL packages (courtesy Signetics International Corporation)

Those i.c.s encapsulated in transistor-like metal cans require much more care in the soldering because the pins or wires are closer. Soldering should be quick, but very effective, and not result in dry joints. Details of printed circuit wiring are given in a companion book in this series and show how the copper layouts are made for i.c.s.

Circuits encapsulated in a resin block, and generally described as integrated circuit modules, require the same kind of care and treatment as any other i.c. If a heat sink forms part of the unit, then sufficient support must be given to take the weight and strain away from the connecting pins. The rules for position of mounting these can be found in Chapter 5.

7 Electromechanical devices

Among the most frequently used electromechanical components, the most commonly used are switches, which for some often mysterious reasons elude the scriptures of most textbooks; they are assumed to be self-explanatory or dismissed as common knowledge not worthy of explanation. This is really a sad omission.

The purpose of a simple switch is to prevent or enable current continuation through a circuit; a typical everyday example is a torch or household lamp. The choice of two states, on or off, is the basis on which logic switching circuits in computers is founded. The switch is usually inserted in the live or 'hot' line of a circuit leading from the power source, as shown in Fig. 40. However, other types of switching circuits are frequently used to select current paths through specially designed component networks of different types.

Fig. 40. Switching

On-off switching of a load using one switch

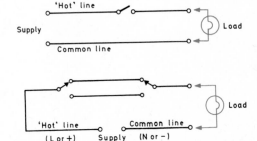

Fig. 41. Switching

On-off switching of a load using two change-over switches

Fig. 41 shows a simple two-path selector generally called a change-over, double-throw, or two-way switch. In this example two of these switches are used to achieve independent control of one load, a lamp,

81

from two positions. The arrowhead on each represents the wiper or movable arm, which selects the required path. Of course, switches can be arranged to select almost any combination or number of paths, limited only by the physical capacity to make a sufficient number

Fig. 42. Switching

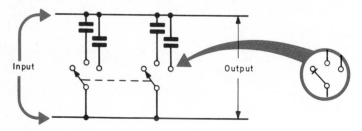

Selection of different component values by using a multi-way rotary switch. These two are shown ganged. Inset shows a made-before-break wiper, used to prevent click noises

available on one switch assembly. A two-pole, 3-way arrangement is shown. in Fig. 42, selecting different capacitors for the circuit. More complex types can have several banks of switches, called wafers, on one rotary mechanical assembly, sometimes called a 'detent mechanism'.

The photograph shows a sample selection of these with the detent mechanism on the left. These wafers are of a variety of sizes and the detent mechanism would need to be tailored to the needs of each complete switch. In most cases the wafer is made from a thin sheet of phenolic resin based material (s.r.b.p.) or ceramic; some of the more

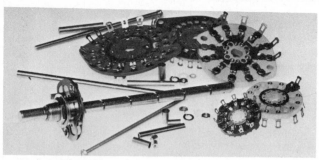

Rotary wafer switches are made up to individual requirements from a range of components: the rotator assembly (left), studding and spacers (centre), and wafer contact assemblies (right). Notice the different styles of wafer made from phenolic resin board or ceramics (courtesy Diamond-H Controls Ltd.)

82

recent types have a base material of glass-filled diallyl phthalate which provides a more stable and tougher wafer at relatively lower cost; it is resistant to current leakage problems in adverse environments. The contacts are silver plated to prevent adverse effects from oxidation.

Since the switching arrangement can often be made up to the constructor's choice, within certain reasonable limits, it is important when ordering to state your exact requirements, including the correct length of wafer-end spindle, pairs of studding for bolting the wafers to the detent mechanism and the appropriate spacers for mounting between each wafer. The wafers are usually made with a set number of combinations of contacts, such as those shown in Table 12; the choice of group will depend on the size of assembly used. It is possible to obtain assemblies already made up, some of which may not have the common number of contacts. It is necessary to know exactly what the switch is expected to do in your application. The description will be by reference to a number of 'poles' (switch wipers) and a number of ways for each pole; all switches arranged on one wafer will be the same. Notice that, for one family of wafers there is a common product of the number of poles times the number of ways (e.g. 2-pole, 6-way, $2 \times 6 = 12$).

Table 12. Examples of the range of switching wafers available

GROUP 1 Standard ready assembled switches	GROUP 2 Standard size wafer kits	GROUP 3 Miniature size kits
(break before make)	(break before make)	(break before make)
1-pole, 12-way	1-pole, 12-way	1-pole, 12-way
2-pole, 6-way	2-pole, 6-way	2-pole, 6-way
3-pole, 4-way	3-pole, 4-way	3-pole, 4-way
4-pole, 3-way	4-pole, 3-way	4-pole, 3-way
	6-pole, 2-way	6-pole, 2-way
	1-pole, 12-way open circuit, 11 ways shorted	
	(make before make) Range as above.	(make before break) 1-pole, 11-way 1-pole, 12-way 2-pole, 5-way 2-pole, 6-way

In Table 12, group 1 includes ready made assemblies that are sometimes called 'wavechange' switches.

In addition to those shown in Table 12, there are other less common combinations involving partially shorted and partially open contact arrangements which are custom designed and made and rarely found in popular component catalogues. The constructor is likely to find these on surplus equipment that has been released by the telephone or government establishments.

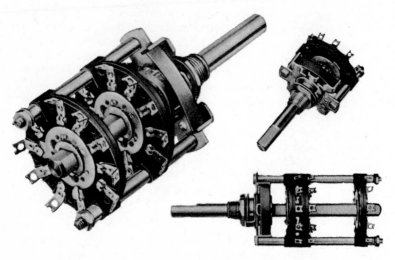

An example of a two-bank wafer switch assembly, each bank having a single-pole 12-way switch (courtesy N.S.F. Ltd.)

The arrangement of tags on the back of a four-pole, 3-way wafer is shown in Fig. 43 and an example of how two poles are drawn in a circuit diagram is shown in Fig. 42. They are made so that the wiper makes contact with the next path in its rotary sequence before breaking from the previous contact; this is called make-before-break (mbb). The purpose of this is to provide a smooth transition from one path to the next without the risk of 'clicks' of noise breaking through.

Fig. 43. Switches

An example of a simple ready-assembled rotary wafer switch; this is a four-pole 3-way type

Four wiper tags in centre

Each contact group round periphery

Those switches listed in group 2 include break-before-make types (bbm); make-before-break types can be obtained in these categories. An interesting wafer is the last mentioned in this group, which provides a path between the wiper and all the selection paths except one so that the constructor can isolate one path at a time on rotation, the inverse of a normal single-pole 12-way selector. Miniature versions of both of these groups can be obtained in many types, but allowance should be made for fewer functions on some wafers because of the restricted space available.

Accessories that make wafer assemblies extremely versatile include add-on screens, which are metal plates that can be fitted to the studding between wafers to prevent unwanted interaction of signals. Non-operational wafers, called 'dummies' can also be fitted to help in the mounting of small components connected to the switching wafer. A ganged mains on-off switch in a totally enclosed moulding can also be fitted so that it operates simultaneously with the detent mechanism.

Wafer switch assemblies are the most versatile used and are found on almost every kind of apparatus from domestic entertainment to sophisticated industrial control equipment. Where automation is required a wafer can be operated by an electromagnetic rotary solenoid, called a Ledex motor. By magnetic attraction a plate is made to rotate through one step of a standard wafer, so by linking this to a spindle and ratchet mechanism it can step the wafer from one position to the next on application of a pulse voltage. Another automatic stepping switch is the telephone exchange type uniselector which is a different form of rotating switch, using a ratchet and pawl mechanism and large rotating wiper blades in a semicircular arc of several contacts.

The main hazard of all of these switches is their vulnerability to dust and dirt which can seriously effect contact efficiency, more so in warm operating conditions which attracts dirt. If dirty contacts are giving trouble, a quick cure can be temporarily effected by rotating the

Fig. 44. Switches

A two-pole changeover switch (dpdt) made in slide or toggle style has the connections in two distinct parts. The wiper is the centre connection.

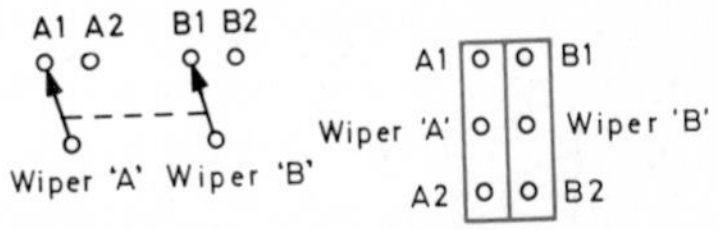

control knob a few times. A better and long-term solution is to clean the contacts with a proprietary switch cleaner solution; never use flammable liquids such as petrol or paraffin, or carbon tetrachloride which can apparently cure the fault, only to give rise to worse faults in the future.

Toggle, rocker, push-button and slide switches rarely have the capacity for more that two poles, although some four-pole toggle switches may be found in special applications such as military equipment. Table 13 summarises the types most often used. Fig. 44 shows the connections of a typical double-pole double-throw switch.

Some changeover toggle switches can be set in a centre neutral position where no connection is made. This is very useful where only a quick selection of one path is required, then switched off or transferred to another path. Two on-off switches are effectively incorporated into one assembly with one common wiper.

Table 13. Toggle, rocker, push-button and slide switches

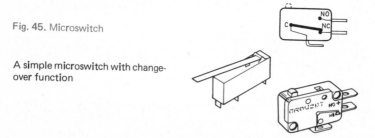

Description	*Function*	
Single-pole, single-throw (SPST)	Single on-off	
Double-pole, single-throw (DPST)	Double-gang on-off	
Single-pole, double-throw (SPDT)	Single changeover	
Double-pole, double-throw (DPDT)	Double-gang, changeover	

These functions are provided on many other types of switch such as the lever keyswitch, microswitch and magnetic reed proximity switch. The microswitch shown in Fig. 45 is operated by moving a spring strip up or down, usually under the influence of the position of a moving object in a machine. The switch can be a normal open (NO) or normal closed (NC) type or may be both in a changeover arrangement.

Fig. 45. Microswitch

A simple microswitch with changeover function

Reed switches can be operated by the relative position and polarity of a permanent or electromagnet (Fig. 46). By reversing the polarity of the magnet, the opposite function will result. In place of a permanent magnet, an electromagnet can be used with the same effect; by feeding a continuously alternating current of very low frequency, or a pulse train system of either polarity, the electromagnetic reed switch becomes a very useful reed relay. The polarity will determine whether the contacts open or close; a changeover type can also be used, in which the moving contact is normally in a neutral position. The greatest advantage of the reed switch is that it is sealed in a glass capsule making it permanently immune to dirt problems. Where a coil is used as the magnetic source, the reed switch capsule is inserted inside.

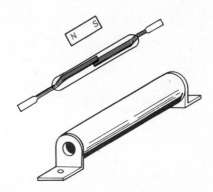

Fig. 46. Reed switch

A reed switch operated by energising the coil; the reed contact part is inserted inside the coil

Another kind of manually operated switch is the 'thumbwheel' type (Fig. 47). It is easy to imagine a bank of these mounted side by side, giving a direct readout of switch number or selected position. Each switch digit is operated independently and connections are made via a plug-in printed circuit type connector on the back. Any switch in a bank can be quickly removed for servicing or replacement, without having to dismantle the equipment or desolder the connections.

Fig. 47. Thumbwheel switch

One section of a thumbwheel switch. Several can be bolted together to make up a multiple digit indicator switch. Connection is made via the printed circuit type contacts at the rear of the module

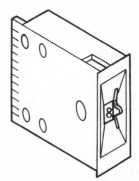

As an extension of the principle of the magnetically operated reed switch relay, the conventional relay also uses a coil, but requires a moving armature to operate the contacts. The armature is attracted to an electromagnet and simultaneously moves the wiper contact between

87

two other contacts, so forming a changeover set. In the same way contact sets can be made as 'make' or 'break' contacts.

A subminiature thumbweel switch made up into a bank of three groups of digits; a single unit is shown on the right (courtesy Birch-Stolec Ltd.)

Fig. 48 shows how a basic relay would be shown in a circuit diagram. The number inside the box represents the resistance of the coil in ohms. Alongside are shown the three types of contact set as they would be drawn; the physical arrangment of each type in a stack with arrowheads indicating which are the moving wiper contacts. An example

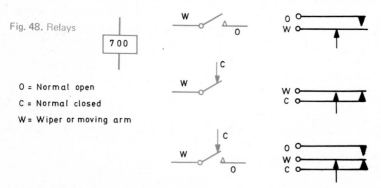

Fig. 48. Relays

O = Normal open
C = Normal closed
W = Wiper or moving arm

Circuit symbols for the relay coil (top) and the make, break and changeover contacts. Physical arrangement of contacts on the 600 and 3000 type relays are shown right

of a stacking arrangement is shown in Fig. 49. Each wiper is moved by an insulated push-pin, sometimes fitted to the appropriate contact arms. When the armature is made to operate, the pins simultaneously move all the wiper blades.

Fig. 49. Relay contacts

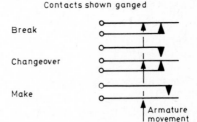

Contacts shown ganged

Break

Changeover

Make

Armature movement

An example of how a stack of ganged contacts might be arranged for simultaneous operation, using insulated pins shown by the arrows

This type of wiper contact assembly is commonly used on Post Office series 600 and 3000 relays, which require 12 to 50 V to operate them depending on the physical loading of the contact assembly. An example is shown in Fig. 50. The compact enclosed types operate

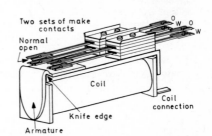

Fig. 50. Contacts

Arrangement of two sets of make contacts on a 600 type relay

Two sets of make contacts

Normal open

Coil

Coil connection

Knife edge

Armature

under the same principles and have been designed in a wide range of types for various d.c. and a.c. operating voltages. Normal standard contacts are not intended to carry more than about two amps at voltages of less than about 100V. They are connected by means of

Fig. 51. Compact relay

Compact relay often sealed in a transparent plastic case

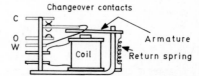

Changeover contacts

Armature

Coil

Return spring

solder tags, or pins for plug-in applications. Fig. 51 shows the solder tag type. The standard contact is dome-shaped as shown in Fig. 52a and is usually plated with platinum or silver for low contact resistance and immunity to adverse effects from oxidation. The heavy duty type (Fig. 52b) is circular in section and only slightly rounded in profile at the contact surface. It is larger than the standard size and rated to carry small a.c. mains currents at up to 250V. Pitting is the worst enemy of all contacts and is caused by sparking. Once pitting has set in, there is no cure other than replacement of the contacts; it is better to suppress the sparking, particularly on heavy duty contacts, by fitting a suppressor, made up either from a 100nF (0.1μF) capacitor or a series combination of capacitor and discharge leakage resistor of about 220 ohms 1 watt.

Fig. 52. Relay contacts

Fig. 52a. Normal set of light-duty contacts for low current applications

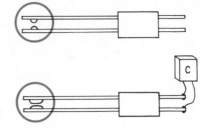

Fig. 52b. Heavy duty contacts sometimes used for mains supply applications. A spark-quench capacitor is shown

Relays that are exposed to atmospheric dust will become soiled quickly, giving rise to intermittent operation of the contacts. Sparking can also occur shortening their life. Where possible, it is best to enclose the relay contacts or used factory sealed units. It is never a wise plan to attempt adjustment of the contact strips unless you have been properly instructed in the art with the correct tools and you know the full reasons and implications of doing so. It should not be necessary to make such adjustments to relays that are new or have been properly protected in sealed cases.

Some Post Office types are fitted with extra large cores at one end of the coil assembly to provide slow-to-operate or slow-to-release facilities. These are shown in the companion volume on *Electronic Diagrams*. The timing of contact closure can be set by the adjustment screw in the armature face. These facilities are not usually available on sealed units. The armature is returned to its normal position by the tension in the contact spring set, which should not be disturbed, whereas in sealed units there is a separate return spring.

The coil ratings given in manufacturers' data sheets are nominal operating voltages; the actual operating voltage may be slightly lower, while the release voltage can be even lower. The resistance due to inertia is such that it will require more to operate than to release, in order to overcome the tension of the return spring. The current rating will depend on the d.c. resistance of the coil and should never be allowed to exceed the recommended maximum current rating of the driving transistor or other switching device.

90

Appendix

Common abbreviations applied to components

Transistors, diodes, thyristors, triacs

Collector	c	Base 1	b1
Base	b	Base 2	b2
Emitter	e	Anode	a
Drain	d	Cathode	k
Gate	g	Main terminal	mt
Source	s	Internal shield	s
Intrinsic region	i		

Valves, cathode ray tubes

Anode	a	Filament	f
Grid	g1	Internal shield	s
Screen grid	g2	Top cap	TC
Suppressor grid	g3	Internal diode anode	d
Cathode	k	Trigger electrode	t
Heater	h	Heater centre tap	h_{ct}

Note: Where two valves are contained in the same envelope, they may be distinguished by a prime symbol (') next to the abbreviations of one set of electrodes.

Logic integrated circuits

Gate	G		
Astable	AS	Two circuits or devices	Dual
Bistable	BS	Three circuits	Triple
Monostable	MS	Four circuits	Quad
Strobe	st	Six circuits	Hex
Binary coded decimal	BCD	Inverter	Inv
Decoder	Dec	Expander	Exp
Flip-Flop	F-F	Comparator	Comp
Read-only memory	ROM	Random access memory	RAM
Synchroniser	Sync	Encoder	Enc
Decade counter	Dec-co	Reset-Set	R-S
Exclusive-OR	Exc-OR	Amplifiers	Amp
AND gate	&	OR gate	$\underline{1}$
NAND gate	$\overline{\&}$	NOR gate	$\overline{1}$

Other components

Centre-tap	ct	Screen connection	scr
Earth	E	Aerial	AE
Common	com	Top cap connection	TC
Make before break	mbb	Break before make	bbm
Single-pole on-off	SPST	Single-pole changeover	SPDT
Double-pole on-off	DPST	Double-pole changeover	DPDT
Intermediate frequency	i.f.	Radio frequency	r.f.
Audio frequency	a.f.	High frequency	h.f.
Very high frequency	v.h.f.	Ultra high frequency	u.h.f.

Fuse Wire Rating

Rated Current (A)	Tinned Copper Wire S.W.G.
5	35
10	28
15	26
20	24
30	22

Standard Abbreviations of Multiples and Submultiples

Term	Abbreviation	Multiple factor	Applications
giga	G	$\times 10^{12}$	GHz
mega	M	$\times 10^{6}$	MHz, MΩ, MW, MV
kilo	k	$\times 10^{3}$	kHz, kΩ, kW, kV
deci	d	$\times 10^{-1}$	dB
centi	c	$\times 10^{-2}$	cm
milli	m	$\times 10^{-3}$	mm, mW, mV, mA, mH, ms
micro	μ	$\times 10^{-6}$	μV, μA, μH, μF, $\mu\Omega$, μs
nano	n	$\times 10^{-9}$	nF, ns
pico	p	$\times 10^{-12}$	pF

Units and Abbreviations

Hertz	Hz	Frequency (formerly cycles per second)
Ohm	Ω	Resistance, impedance, reactance
Watt	W	Power
Volt	V	Electromotive force, potential difference
Bel	B	Ratio of signal levels
Metre	m	Metric length, wavelength
Ampere	A	Current
Henry	H	Inductance
Second	s	Time
Farad	F	Capacitance
Coulomb	C	Quantity of charge

Conversion of British Standard Wire Gauge to Inches and Millimetres

S.W.G.	Diameter (in)	Diameter (mm)	Copper wire current rating (A)
0	0.324	8.2	
2	0.276	7.0	
4	0.232	5.9	
6	0.192	4.9	
8	0.160	4.06	
10	0.128	3.25	15.44
12	0.104	2.64	10.19
14	0.080	2.03	6.32
16	0.064	1.63	3.86
18	0.048	1.22	2.17
20	0.036	0.92	1.22
22	0.028	0.71	0.73
24	0.022	0.56	0.456
25	0.020	0.51	0.377
26	0.018	0.46	0.305
27	0.0164	0.42	0.253
28	0.0148	0.38	0.206
29	0.0136	0.35	0.174
30	0.0124	0.32	0.145
31	0.0116	0.29	0.127
32	0.0108	0.27	0.110
33	0.0100	0.25	0.094
34	0.0092	0.23	0.080
35	0.0084	0.21	0.066
36	0.0076	0.19	0.054
37	0.0068	0.17	0.043
38	0.0060	0.15	0.034
39	0.0052	0.13	0.025
40	0.0048	0.12	0.021
41	0.0044	0.11	0.018
42	0.0040	0.10	0.015
43	0.0036	0.09	0.012
44	0.0032	0.08	0.0096
45	0.0028	0.07	0.0074
46	0.0024	0.06	0.0054
47	0.0020	0.05	0.0037
48	0.0016	0.04	0.0024
49	0.0012	0.03	0.0013
50	0.0010	0.025	0.0010

BA Screw Threads and drilling sizes

BA	Tapping Drills		Clearance Drills	
	Number size	Metric size	Number size	Metric size
0	9	5.0	Letter C	6.15
2	24	3.9	12	4.8
4	34	2.8	26	3.75
6	43	2.35	32	3.0
8	50	1.8	43	2.35
10	54	1.4	48	1.95

Note: These are the most common sizes used in electronics

Index

99

100

For the Beginner

BEGINNER'S GUIDE TO ELECTRONICS — 3rd Edition

T.L. SQUIRES, CEng, MIERE
C.M. DEASON, MSc, BSc

The third edition of this highly
successful work of reference
written for those entering the
diverse field of electronics. The
text has been completely revised
and brought up to date with much
new material added to include any
new developments. The subject is
dealt with non-mathematically
with emphasis placed on
illustrative examples.

240 pages 192 x 126mm
Illustrated 1974 0 408 00126 7

BEGINNER'S GUIDE TO TRANSISTORS — 2nd Edition

J.A.REDDIHOUGH' revised by
I.R. SINCLAIR, BSc, CEng,
MIEE, MInstP.

Describes what transistors are,
how they work, the many types
available and their many applications. A full revision has ensured
that this second edition incor-
porates the latest developments in
integrated circuits, and logic
principles have been introduced.

160 pages 192 x 126mm
Illustrated 1975 0 408 00145 3

For further details of this series
please write to

NEWNES - BUTTERWORTHS

EVEN MORE BOOKS FOR THE CONSTRUCTOR ON THE WAY

PRACTICAL ELECTRONIC PROJECT BUILDING

Alan Ainslie   Morris A. Colwell

A concise but informative guide to some of the current popular methods of construction and techniques employed in home construction. Contains hints on finishing and fault-finding methods.

Contents: Tools and Basic Skills. Kits and Components. Layout and Wiring. Wiring Boards. Printed Circuit Boards. Metalwork and Cases. Presentation and Finishing. Testing and Fault-Finding. Index.

PROJECT PLANNING AND BUILDING

Morris A. Colwell

Provides a wide range of ideas and guidance on the planning and building of projects. Emphasis is laid mainly on planning and design, since it is here that a good circuit starts its life, first from the viewpoint of performance and secondly, a well-designed circuit is easy to service or modify, as necessary.

Contents: Planning. Working with Tools. Component Board Layout. Case Design and Layout. Case and Chassis Construction. Assembly and Wiring. Useful Tables. Index.

For further details please write to
NEWNES - BUTTERWORTHS